greatsex for life

ESSENTIAL TECHNIQUES

greatsex forlife

ESSENTIAL TECHNIQUES

Linda Sonntag

HAMLYN

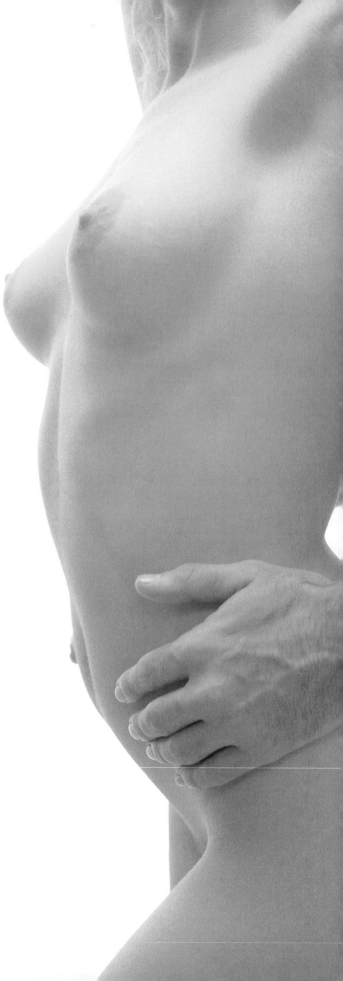

great**sex**
for**life**

ESSENTIAL
TECHNIQUES

C O N T E N T S

ISBN 0 600 59427 0

The textual material in this book is an abridged
and updated version of the following titles which
were previously published by Hamlyn:
Making Love 1992
Keep Love Alive 1993

WARNING: With the prevalence of AIDS and other
sexually transmitted diseases, if you do not practise safe
sex you are risking your life and your partner's life.

Thirty years on from the advent of the Pill, which opened an

era of greater sexual awareness, we have more freedom of

sexual choice than ever before in our personal lives. Yet for

many people such liberty poses more questions than it

answers, and as knowledge grows, so too do expectations in

our sexual relationships. Lovers worry about whether they are

living up to their partner's expectations, question whether

their feelings are 'normal', need information on such subjects

as AIDS, or simply wonder what they can do to enjoy their

love life more.

Great Sex For Life - Essential Techniques explains the

mystery of sexual attraction, how you can build and

strengthen your relationship, and throw aside your inhibitions

to gain new and deeper

enjoyment with your partner.

It explains subjects such as

masturbation, orgasm and sexual

positions in clear straightforward

language, and the text is illustrated

with specially commissioned

photography. And, for those who merely have a query about

love or sex but haven't found the right person to ask, the book

also provides reassuring answers on subjects such as

contraception, health and sexual problems.

Relationships

Our attitudes to sex and sexuality are shaped both by the society and the age in which we live, and by the influence of our immediate family. Understanding the roots of our feelings enables us to overcome inhibitions and form deeper and more satisfying sexual relationships.

Sexual attraction

What is it that suddenly makes two people light up the instant they set eyes on each other? Why does it often take only a few seconds of being in each other's company for a man and a woman to feel irresistibly drawn together?

One moment you may be leading a normal, seemingly uneventful life, and the next, you may find yourself exchanging glances with someone who makes you feel bewildered, excited, elated, charged with nervous energy. Moments such as these never fail to catch us unawares, and their force and suddenness can change the whole course of our lives. To an onlooker, the phenomenon of sexual attraction often resembles nothing so much as madness. Within a short time of meeting, two rational people are capable of promising to stay together for upwards of half a century. The lovers themselves may be too impatient to analyse how they can possibly be so sure of each other; it is enough for them to be in love, and they are content to attribute their new-found state of high excitement to immense good fortune.

Sexual attraction is often instant.

Because of this it seems involuntary, and is therefore often put down to a superhuman agency such as 'luck' or 'destiny'. Mythology would have us believe that attraction is directed by the gods and that it strikes out of the blue in the form of Cupid's fatal dart. The magic potion on the tip of the dart suspends consciousness, will and judgement, and leaves its victims in a state of hopeless intoxication. It is still commonly believed today that sexual attraction is something irrational and beyond our power to influence or control, yet studies made by psychiatrists and behavioural scientists have found that it is far from being the random and inexplicable phenomenon that it seems. Newly published evidence suggests that we are unconsciously, and at a glance, capable of making fairly accurate judgements about not only other people's social and economic standing, but also about their emotional background. The 'miracle' of love at first sight really does exist, but what is truly miraculous is our own unconscious process of selection.

Opposites attract. This common belief has been borne out by numerous successful partnerships. Introverts and extroverts are often drawn together because the quiet strength of the one complements the liveliness of the other. The extrovert sees the introvert as a rock, an anchor in a storm; and the introvert sees the extrovert as fire, warmth and light. Their lives would feel incomplete without each other; they act as a unique foil for each other's characters, and they do not compete, because the sum of all their attributes seems to form a perfect whole.

Like also attracts like, in terms of character, appearance or family background, as other partnerships show. In every relationship there will undoubtedly be some points of similarity, and others where the partners are poles apart. Whether the relationship succeeds depends not only on getting the perfect balance, but also on keeping the balance as each partner grows and develops, possibly at different speeds and in different directions.

Physical appearance is a more obvious factor in the complex signals of sexual attraction. However, contrary to popular belief, people are not automatically attracted to the most beautiful member of the opposite sex, although there is broad agreement about what constitues physical beauty in both men and women. Instead, they are drawn to people who are in the same league of attractiveness as themselves.

Two experiments illustrate this. In one, a group of people, some of whom were physically very attractive and others less so, were shown a series of photographs and asked to select the person with whom they would most like to go out. Only the most attractive people picked beautiful partners. In the other experiment, people were given individual photographs of men and women who were married. They were asked to rate them for good looks, and then to place them in pairs. Most agreed on the degree of attractiveness of each person, and remarkably, the group had put together several couples who were really married.

A common background

A fascinating experiment is carried out by the Institute of Family Therapy (UK) with its new recruits. Before the individuals in the group have got to know anything about each other, a psychiatrist asks them to walk round the room, and without exchanging any words, pick a partner whom they feel could be a 'missing member' of their own family. Each couple then selects a further couple to form 'families' of four. This process complete, the psychiatrist then asks them to talk together to find out why they have picked each other.

Individuals single out others with similar backgrounds as the experiment clearly displays. A group of four might find, for instance, that all their fathers spent a significant period of their childhood away from home, whereas another group might discover that the individuals all came from families where there was a difficulty with expressing affection or anger, or where everyone was expected to keep a 'stiff upper lip' and to conceal their true emotions.

People may be drawn together because of similarities in the way in which their families functioned, as the exercise demonstrates, but the knack we have of recognizing these similarities, just by looking at another person, is uncanny. How do we do it? Psychiatrists explain the mysterious 'chemistry' of attraction by suggesting that our childhood experiences – the reactions we learned to give in various situations – have over the years 'hardened' into habitual expressions, gestures, postures and movements, and it is these signals to which we respond as adults.

In our quest for the familiar we also seek out the same faults or weaknesses in other people that played a formative role in our own childhood. The writer Edna O'Brien put it like this: 'I have a big flaw in that I'm attracted to thin, tall, good-looking men who have one common denominator. They must be lurking bastards.' If a loved father harbours a lurking bastard, then love may always be associated in the mind of the child with a tendency towards cruelty. When the child grows up, the chances are that she will find herself attracted to men who display this irresistible characteristic.

Body language

The language of the body – expressions, gestures, the way we stand and the way we move – is for the most part unconscious, as is our understanding of the body language of others. We don't have to think about it to realise that a man who is pinning a woman against a wall at a party and leering down her cleavage is showing aggressive sexual interest. Nor do we need a degree in psychology to work out that the woman, if she has her arms crossed over her chest and is frowning at him, does not welcome his attention. These two people are giving off signals loud and clear that cannot be misread.

Nerves or lack of confidence may mean that we sometimes give off the wrong signals. If you go alone to a party hoping to meet interesting people and then sit hunched in a corner with your legs tightly wrapped around each other, your arms folded and your head lowered, you should not be surprised if people can't detect the friendly and talkative person you really are under your hostile exterior. The people who invite approach are the ones who stand and sit in a relaxed and open way and appear alert to their surroundings and unafraid to engage in eye contact. If you have the confidence to look as friendly and as interesting as you feel, conversation will practically initiate itself.

Once contact has been made between two people who are attracted to each other, the signs come thick and fast. The eyes show vulnerability – a conflict between fear and desire. They want to look and, at the same time, to look away. If both people are shy, they will exchange only the briefest of glances to begin with, looking in between times fixedly at the carpet or at their hands. Shy, sidelong glances, often called 'sheep's eyes' follow, until one person gains enough courage to look for longer. As confidence grows, eye contact becomes more prolonged: couples stare at each other, and 'devour' each other with their eyes. They also begin to look at other parts of each other's faces, particularly at the mouth, and then at other parts of the body, but all the while checking back to the eyes to assess their partner's reactions to such scrutiny.

People who are interested in each other sit or stand facing each other, not sideways on, which indicates some reserve. Their attitudes to each other are open, with no barriers, such as arms across the body. Their faces are tilted towards each other with wide eyes and eyebrows raised, and they smile a lot with their mouths open. There are generally more gestures.

Hands, arms and shoulders

are employed to express vitality, as are eyebrows and lips, and the tongue is more active than usual, becoming a particular focus of attention. The pair will stand closer together than is normal, and at the slightest excuse there will be physical contact, usually in the guise of a gesture of support, such as helping a woman into a coat or protecting her from someone passing in a hurry.

As the conversation progresses

with the exchange of shared likes and dislikes, there may be a temptation to suppress true opinions in order to avoid the danger of disagreement bringing the budding relationship to a premature end. People who have just met and who like each other tend to nod a lot in enthusiastic agreement, even if their views diverge. But if the disagreements are fundamental, eventually these will put a dampener on the initial attraction. Other people who are more confident make playful use of argument to pepper their conversation, and this is particularly attractive to those who like daring characters, though it may frighten off more timid prospective partners.

Sexual signals

When a baby is born, only its genitals distinguish male from female, but as the child grows into an adult, it develops distinctive sexual characteristics that signal its gender to prospective mates.

Many of the body's gender signals have evolved over more than a million years. When early man began to depend more on hunting for food and less on the gathering of roots and berries, labour was divided between the sexes. The females, who were almost always either pregnant or nursing their offspring, could not accompany the males in pursuit of game, and so the nomadic way of life was replaced by a settled one. The females continued to forage near the settlement for food, while the males roamed further afield. As the males got more adept at hunting, their bodies developed to suit its requirements.

The body of modern man displays the lifestyle of generations past, despite the fact that in most parts of the world men no longer live by hunting and women's lives are greatly less restricted by breeding. Men are taller, more muscular and heavier. They are built for running faster and for carrying heavier loads. They are broad-shouldered, with stronger arms, which makes them better equipped for using weapons. They have broader chests and larger lungs, making them capable of greater exertion, and they have stronger skulls and jaws to protect them more efficiently against attack.

The special features of the female physique are her wider pelvis, which is tilted slightly backwards to facilitate child-bearing, her longer belly and thicker thighs, geared towards carrying the foetus, and her swollen breasts, developed for suckling her young. The wide pelvis means that the thighs start from further apart, and the female's crotch gap contrasts with the male crotch bulge. The angle of the legs, which slope together towards the knees, and the fleshy protuberances of breast and buttocks, make running less easy than for the male. The narrower shoulders mean that the arms hang at the sides, whereas the more muscular male stands with his arms hanging away from his body. The female physique is thus less well developed for carrying, but the female forearm can swing out from her side to a much greater angle than can that of a man.

The differences in the structure of male and female arms and legs means that each sex moves in a quite distinct way. It is something we take for granted until a male comedian draws attention to it by mimicking a woman or an effeminate man.

There are other sexual signals that have nothing to do with our evolutionary past as hunters and breeders. They act purely to emphasize the bearer's sex. The male has a deeper voice and a prominent Adam's apple. His body is generally hairier, although the hair on the top of the head may thin and disappear in later life. The female is characterised by a fleshier body, with smooth spherical breasts and buttocks echoed by rounder knees, shoulders and cheeks, fuller lips, and a softer, almost hairless skin. It has been said that whereas the male erogenous zones (parts of the body that respond to sexual stimulation) are primarily the genitals, mouth and hands, the entire female body is an erogenous zone, because the skin is so sensitive. In an effort to make their skin even more appealing to the opposite sex, many women shave their armpits and spend a great deal of money in beauty clinics having 'unsightly' body hair removed.

Display signals are used in the animal kingdom as a sexual invitation. The female monkey or ape signals her willingness to copulate by presenting to the male her rump and genitals, which are often highly coloured. Since adult humans normally encounter each other face to face, now that we no longer walk on all-fours, the female body has developed frontal display signs that are genital mimics. The rounded breasts are reminiscent of the buttocks, and the full lips represent the labia.

When man began to walk upright he adopted the first piece of clothing ever to be worn – the loincloth. As soon as he got up from all-fours he exposed his genitals to everyone he met, and to eliminate the resulting inappropriate sexual signal, he concealed them behind a 'fig-leaf'. The climate in which early man developed did not necessitate the wearing of clothes for protection against heat or cold, so the first garment was donned purely for reasons of modesty.

Protective clothing was adopted as man moved away from his early home into other climates. Our clothing, today as always, reflects the attitude of the society in which we live towards sexuality. For example, in some Arab countries, women are swathed in voluminous robes from head to toe so that only their eyes are visible.

Clothing used in the West to emphasise sexuality includes the brassiere and the corset. Men have drawn attention to their brawny shoulders with shoulder pads and epaulettes, and to their genitals by the use of the codpiece, the sheathed gun or dagger at the hip, and even the sporran, with its mimic of pubic hair. Today, tight jeans over a bulging crotch give off the same message.

Shyness and inhibitions

Shyness of strangers has its roots in earliest childhood. Babies bury their heads against their mothers' shoulders when spoken to by unfamiliar people, young children hide in their mothers' skirts, while adolescent girls giggle and put their hands to their faces. Most adults still suffer some apprehension on moving into an unfamiliar social situation.

To walk alone into a room full of strangers engaged in animated conversation with each other and to integrate with them requires courage. The fear of being the outsider in a foreign territory is a strong one, and the newcomer usually expresses the need to protect himself against a strange environment by forming a barrier across his body. Women frequently touch their hair, adjust their clothing, or check their bracelet, watch or bag. Men can often be seen entering a pub rubbing their hands together as they walk up to the bar. All these gestures, unconscious though they may be, form a temporary barrier across the body and betray the nervousness the newcomer feels. The shyness of the outsider needs to be conquered each time a new social situation is broached; the more practice you get, the better you will be able to disguise your nervousness.

Shyness resulting from fear and desire characterises the beginning of most sexual relationships, but after this has been overcome and the relationship is established, inhibition may still prevent true intimacy. A couple who are locked inside themselves, whether through fear or distaste of their own sexuality, or through lack of courage, imagination or knowledge, may copulate together throughout their married life without really communicating, and without ever properly getting to know the far reaches and deep subtleties of each other's personalities.

This situation suits some couples, but if one of the partners becomes more adventurous, he or she may seek the necessary stimulation elsewhere. True satisfaction comes not from travelling incognito on parallel rails, but from openness in all aspects of your life together. No one can expect to ignite the fire of passion without a spark, and you can't get sparks without friction, or friction without contact.

The word 'intercourse' means 'dealings in which there is an exchange of communication'. Sexual intercourse at its best is a communion in which feelings – physical and emotional – are freely given and received. A free exchange cannot take place if one or both partners are holding back.

Fear of letting go is another major cause of sexual inhibition. To people who have been brought up with the idea that keeping control is the key to success in life, the very sound of the words 'letting go' represents chaos and disaster. This is as true of men as it is of women. Indeed, it is possible to go through the whole of the sex act, including orgasm, without ever giving oneself up to the other person. The result is, 'cold', mechanical sex.

Men who are sexually active

but suffer from the fear of letting go rarely feel the need to feign passion, because erection and ejaculation are 'evidence' of their sexuality. However, for women, the situation is different. A woman may be desperate to show how attractive she finds her partner, and desperate to give herself, but prevented from doing so by her fear of letting go. In order to prove her sexuality, she may therefore act out what she thinks it means by thrashing about, moaning and groaning and even faking orgasms like the actresses in blue movies.

Acting is exhausting, especially in bed, where you are very vulnerable and under close scrutiny. It is not satisfying because it erects a barrier between you and your partner, and if the problem is not tackled soon, it will simply drive you further apart. Allow yourselves unlimited time and absolute privacy. Take things extremely slowly, savouring every touch and caress. Don't force anything, and if one of you feels that the other has made an artificial move – one that smacks of 'getting on with it' – gently stop him or her from continuing and re-establish your bearings. Being uninhibited is doing what you both like, and you are finding out exactly what that is by moving very tentatively, as if you were exploring each other's bodies for the first time.

Touching and closeness

Physical affection is an important form of emotional nourishment for the human baby. The drastic consequences of depriving babies of affection were shown in a study comparing the behaviour and development of babies in two orphanages. The parents of the babies in the first orphanage had been victims of an earthquake; the babies had been suddenly cut off from love and affection and there were not enough nurses to give them prolonged individual attention. These babies cried a lot and showed little interest in food. Their mental and physical development was slow. The babies in the second orphanage had been there since birth and were frequently picked up and cuddled by the staff. Their growth rate was normal, and they were alert and cheerful.

Babies and children thrive on being hugged and cuddled until they reach adolescence, when their developing bodies need privacy and separateness more than closeness. But once they emerge from puberty reorientated as young adults, they begin to seek contact with the opposite sex. Children who grow up in homes where physical affection is a natural part of everyday life usually have few inhibitions as adults about touching and closeness, and little trouble in recreating the warm, nest-like security of their early years in which to form an adult erotic relationship.

To hold your partner tight in a generous hug and completely envelop him or her in your arms is to affirm and accept the way that person is. Hugging and squeezing, holding hands, stroking faces and rubbing backs need not be sexual. In fact, these actions are more often loving, friendly, supportive, comforting, or just part of fooling around. If affectionate contact is part of the way you communicate with your partner, then expressing and receiving sexuality will be easy and natural.

Women love being caressed. The entire surface of a woman's skin, being smooth, delicate and hairless, is highly sensitive and responsive. Women enjoy wearing soft and silky fabrics next to the skin, and they love being stroked and caressed by a gentle partner. Most women stress the importance of touching and closeness in their relationships with men and to their sense of wellbeing in general. Many mention the value of sharing closeness and warmth, the intense pleasure of a fiercely tight embrace, the bliss of falling asleep with bodies entwined, of snuggling up and talking quietly, of lying still and listening to the other person breathe.

According to some women, the female skin is the world's most neglected erogenous zone. Women complain frequently that men are not naturally physically affectionate. Some men are reluctant to touch their partners unless sex is to follow. And if there is no cuddling after sex many women feel used and discarded.

When children are little, boys and girls receive equal amounts of hugging and cuddling from their parents. But as they get older, boys in our society are taught that it is weak to show emotion. In order to grow into big strong men, they must choke back their tears and keep a stiff upper lip. It is fine for girls to weep for sadness or joy, to kiss and embrace, to be effusive and demonstrative, but boys must restrict themselves to handshakes, and, at the most, a pat or slap on the back.

This means that while women often kiss and hug their friends, the only place where it is acceptable for men to show affection for each other is on the football pitch; and while most women long for close loving contact with their partners, fewer men can break out of the tactile isolation in which society has imprisoned them in order to give or receive it.

Many men have reservations about touching and closeness, even though they recognize the importance of physical contact for women. Some dislike women 'hanging round' them, which they see as a sign of insecurity. Some are embarrassed to show affection out of a fear of not appearing masculine enough or being childish. In general, men also have a faster sexual response than women, and see cuddling and kissing as teasing behaviour unless it leads to sex.

Men and women both need to stop categorizing their feelings. Frustrated women draw a firm line between affection and sex. They feel cheated if they can't have the first without the second. Frustrated men also put their feelings in boxes, but they lump sex and affection together. For them, it's either hands off, or all the way, no compromise. These rigid views are poles apart, and can cause a great deal of unhappiness.

Our feelings don't belong in boxes. They can't be turned on and off at will, as if by flicking a switch. It is ignorant and hurtful for a man who behaves coldly to a woman all day to expect her to be hot the minute they get into bed, and it is equally ignorant and hurtful for a woman to inflame a man and then, when he wants sex, leap away as though she'd been burned.

There are many degrees of affection and sexuality and each stage grows out of the one before. For a couple who are physically and mentally in touch, it is possible to sense these moods as they develop, and to go with them, if the time is right, or to check them without rejection, but with the promise of later fulfilment, if the time is wrong.

In the Bible, if two people have sex together, they are said to 'know' each other. This is no mere euphemism, but an accurate description of good sex. It is quite possible to copulate with someone for years without really 'knowing' who that person is, or feeling 'known' yourself. It is like striking the keys of a piano. Anyone can make sound come out, but you need to learn each note that the individual instrument can produce, and to discover how to put them together, if you want to make music.

Relationships

First-time sex

Losing one's virginity is rarely a sensual experience. The novice is bound to feel nervous and afraid of the unknown as well as excited. It can be such a momentous event that often the identity of the first-time partner is not as important as the loss of virginity. Even though the sex may be bungled – over very quickly if the man is a virgin; slightly uncomfortable if it is the woman's first time – there will probably be a sense of elation afterwards, that this important step towards sexual maturity has been achieved.

Most people are apprehensive

about appearing naked in front of each other for the first time. They fear that their imperfect bodies will be subjected to critical scrutiny and found wanting. Women imagine that their breasts are too small or that their thighs or abdomens are too fat to be desirable, while men worry about puny chests and flabby bellies. The biggest male worry is the size of the penis and though most feel that theirs is too small, men who are very well endowed can also be embarrassed by size. However, the better the couple know and like each other, the less afraid they are likely to feel.

The main problem with first-time couples is that the man

may be so nervous that he cannot get or maintain an erection. In which case, his natural frustration, distress and humiliation are made much worse by the importance of the occasion. Faced with the consummation of his desire, he has proved himself 'impotent', which is all the more galling if it has rarely or never happened before. The woman suffers too. She may feel frustrated, she may doubt that he really wants her after all, but if she really cares for him, her greatest difficulty will be in deciding how to cope with his distress. She can hardly ignore the situation and pretend that nothing is wrong, and trying without success to stimulate an unresponsive penis is likely to increase feelings of alienation and failure and may even cause resentment.

The best course of action is to stop 'trying', and to just hold each other and lie close. Too much overt sympathy on the part of the woman could be interpreted as condescending. After a while, one or the other of you will start talking. As the flaccid penis is most likely to be a temporary problem, the important thing is not to analyse it or worry about it, but to give basic reassurance that you still both like each other. Get up and fetch a drink. Enjoy your new-found intimacy in the way you talk to, look at and touch your partner. Once you are both so relaxed as to have forgotten the problem, desire will probably take you unawares, and this time nerves will be less likely to intervene.

Another male problem that commonly occurs on a first time is that over-excitement triggers premature ejaculation. This is not quite such a blow for the man's self-esteem, especially if penetration has been achieved, but it will leave the woman feeling bewildered and unsatisfied if his embarrassment brings the lovemaking to an abrupt end. After a short rest, the man should be ready to continue, and this time he can concentrate on fully arousing and satisfying his partner before he allows himself to come for a second time.

Male orgasm

Man has the largest penis of any living primate. Unlike the penises of most other mammals, it contains no bone, and relies for the stiffness needed for penetration on three rods of spongy erectile tissue, which respond to stimulation. During arousal, the tissue is engorged with blood, and muscles around the veins contract, producing an erection. In uncircumcized men the glans is partly covered by the loose, thin, smooth and highly sensitive skin of the penis, which is moved back and forth over the shaft during sexual activity. In circumcized men the foreskin has been removed by a surgical operation, usually at birth. Circumcision or the lack of it makes no difference to sexual pleasure; uncircumcized men should pay particular attention to genital hygiene by regular washing under the foreskin, which may trap dirt and harbour infection.

At the point of ejaculation a series of powerful muscular contractions causes semen to spurt from the tip of the penis. There is usually 2–5ml (up to a teaspoonful) of this sticky milky white fluid, of which the sperm content is only two to five percent. Quantity of semen is no indication of fertility, but if there is less than 1ml, there is a possibility that the sperm will not reach the cervix through lack of liquid. The sperm resemble microscopic tadpoles, although 18th-century biologists imagined that they could see minute versions of grown men and women swimming about in the seminal fluid. Semen also contains 32 different chemicals, including vitamin C, vitamin B12, sulphur, zinc and potassium; the Russian Empress Catherine the Great used to swear by it as a morning tonic. The purpose of all this goodness is to nourish the sperm as they make their perilous journey towards fertilization. The seminal fluid acts as a lubricant. The male orgasm lasts about 10 seconds. Afterwards, the muscles at the base of the penis relax and the blood drains away, leaving the erectile tissue flaccid once more.

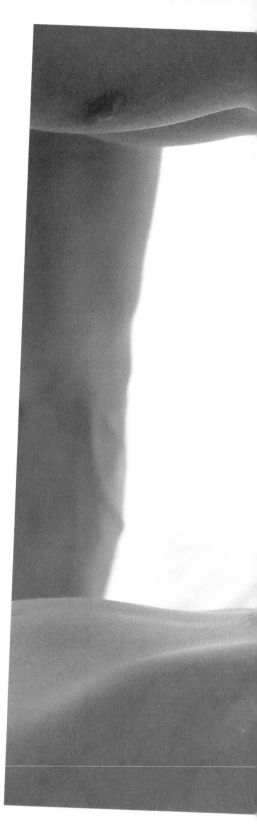

Male orgasm

Female orgasm

The female orgasm, unlike the male orgasm, is not necessary for procreation and exists purely to give pleasure, but this does not mean it is biologically useless. The sexual pleasure that two people find in each other produces an extremely powerful bond. Human beings have the strongest bonding potential of all animals, and it is no coincidence that they also produce the most demanding offspring. Sexuality provides the incentive that offsets the enormous responsibility of bringing up young. As far as researchers can tell, woman is the only female animal capable of orgasm. This peak of sexual enjoyment is a unique evolutionary development, which, when shared, can form the core of an intense and uninhibited relationship.

Sexual arousal is the highly sensitive state in which orgasm is possible. It is a state of heightened awareness that incorporates exhilaration, a fainting feeling, a rushing urgency, supreme sensitivity, well-being, freedom and ecstasy.

The first physical sign of sexual arousal is that the vagina secretes a lubricating fluid. Then the clitoris, the primary organ of female sexuality, a tiny hypersensitive nodule under the labia and above the vaginal opening, becomes hot, erect and swollen. With increasing arousal the labia or vaginal lips also become engorged with blood – they look red and swollen and feel hot and slippery, tender and sensitive. In fact, the female sex organs expand during arousal to match the size of an average-to-large erect penis. The difference is that the responsive tissue in a woman is not as obvious as a man's erection, because it is hidden from sight.

All this can happen without genital contact, in the same way that a man's penis can become erect without being touched. Women can become aroused by psychological stimuli and by being kissed and caressed on any part of their bodies, although the mouth and breasts are particularly sensitive. The exquisite pleasure of arousal lies in its gradual intensification, and a skilful lover will excite his partner to a pitch where her genitals are engorged and lubricated before stimulating them directly with fingers, tongue or penis.

Female orgasm

As arousal heightens, the woman's pulse rate speeds up, her body may arch, her muscles tense and her blood pressure rises. Her face and chest may be flushed and pink, her nipples become erect and her breasts swell. Towards orgasm, the clitoris may become so sensitive that she can no longer bear for it to be touched. In the few seconds before she comes, the woman almost loses consciousness. She is concentrated inwards on herself, her muscles clench, and she may cry out as she loses herself in orgasm.

Orgasm, also called climax or 'coming' is a series of intensely pleasurable muscular contractions which, at the peak of stimulation, grip the engorged tissues surrounding the outer part of the vagina. The sexologists Masters and Johnson measured these contractions and discovered that they occur at intervals of four-fifths of a second – exactly the same rhythm as found in the contractions of the male orgasm. The number of contractions may vary from three to 12; in one particularly intense orgasm, 25 contractions were recorded over 43 seconds. The womb also contracts rhythmically, with spasms moving down in waves towards the cervix. Orgasmic contractions are similar to those experienced during childbirth, although, of course, they are far less severe. Depending on his position, the woman's partner should be able to feel or see her vaginal contractions. External signs of an orgasm in a woman are somewhat akin to rigor mortis, and may even be interpreted by an inexperienced lover as a lack of interest. The woman's whole body becomes rigid and her hands and feet may clench. The blue-movie interpretation of female orgasm, in which women writhe, thrash, arch their backs and grind their pelvises against their partners is inaccurate: both women and men tense into stillness as they come. It is a moment of oblivion, a 'little death', as the French call it.

After orgasm, the woman's chest may be suffused with a red flush or rash. Unless further stimulation and more orgasms are to follow, her body will now very gradually come down from its high to its normal state. Muscle

tension relaxes; blood is released from the engorged tissues of the vagina; the clitoris subsides and withdraws under its hood; the uterus returns to its normal size; pulse, breathing and blood pressure all slow down.

This final phase in sexual response, which Masters and Johnson called 'resolution', may last for around half an hour and can hold feelings very precious for a woman. She may be overwhelmed by love and emotion for her partner to the point of shedding tears, or bathed in tenderness and wellbeing, or there may be a feeling of tremendous light-headedness, fun and vitality.

Women are left with shining eyes and full of happiness after orgasm, and it is just as important for their partners to be able to share in this stage of their lovemaking as in any other. A woman feels let down by a lover who switches off after orgasm and leaves her to come down from her high alone.

Men are often criticised for the way they 'snap out of it' after sex, but there is a physiological reason for this. Men's bodies return within a matter of a few minutes to their unaroused state: breathing and heart rate normalize and the penis rapidly detumesces. A woman's sexual response is far more complex than a man's, and it varies considerably from one individual to the next. Women do not return directly to their unaroused state, but to their pre-orgasmic state: they remain highly sensitive, and capable of further arousal.

Most women feel fully satisfied after one orgasm, and the clitoris may be so sensitive that further stimulation is unpleasant or even painful, but others, and especially those who are used to giving themselves several orgasms in a row during masturbation, may crave more. Masters and Johnson discovered that women are capable of enjoying up to six successive orgasms, if they so wish. Those who have multiple orgasms are not necessarily getting more enjoyment or satisfaction out of sex, and those who have single orgasms should not feel in any way inadequate. The important thing for both partners is to be aware that there is a choice.

Intimacy

The best sex happens between lovers who are getting to know each other intimately, both physically and emotionally, as a result of an insatiable desire to explore each other's bodies and minds. No other activity gives such intense awareness of living in the present.

Many couples have forgotten how to play. Sadly, to them sex seems a serious business, and the various stages that need to be got through to reach the ultimate goal of orgasm are accomplished with efficiency. Sex becomes a habit, a ritual enacted without thought or enthusiasm. But sex is not about fulfilling a contract or proving yourself. It is not a duty or a competition, but an opportunity for sharing spontaneous excitement.

Creative sex is infinite in its variety, like improvisations on a theme. It can be playful, adventurous, erotic. It allows for many moods to express themselves one after another: passion, tenderness, lust, mischievous curiosity – whatever the lovers are feeling. An open approach to making love also allows other things to happen in bed besides sex: it encourages talk and laughter. In bed you can bare your soul as well as your body to your partner; you are also free to lose your inhibitions and just enjoy having fun together.

All human beings are born sensitive, though men may appear to be less sensitive than women because they have been trained not to show their feelings. But tight self-control is an obstacle to intimacy. It often inhibits men in talking about their emotions and, particularly, about love. If you want to get closer, encourage your man to reveal how he feels, to express himself fully in actions and words, by showing and telling him the way you feel. He may need to be convinced that you will not think him 'less of a man' for admitting that he is subject to emotions beyond his control.

Emotional vulnerability in a man is easily underestimated. But whether intercourse can take place or not depends solely on his ability to get and maintain an erection, and sometimes the pressure to 'perform' and the fear of failure can be overwhelming. This is particularly true of first-time sex. A woman can hide her lack of confidence, but in a man it's painfully obvious. The first thing a woman should understand is that if a man has a sexual problem it does not mean that he doesn't want you. If you assume this to be the case and respond with hurt and disappointment, you will only make him feel worse than he does already.

If he loses his erection or ejaculates prematurely, convince him that it's not that important and that you still want him by getting him to satisfy you with his fingers or his tongue. The knowledge that you don't just want him for his erect penis should restore some of his self-esteem, and arousing you and bringing you to orgasm may well renew his desire.

For women, sex at its best involves total physical and emotional response. This is only possible if the feelings between you are positive and any discord or tensions have been resolved. Women love being aroused with kisses and caresses. Their sexual response is individual and highly complex, and though most women are capable of orgasm, and need it for sexual fulfilment, you should not feel disappointed if your partner does not climax the first time you make love with her.

Encourage her to relax, be still and quiet and concentrate solely on the sensations you are giving her. Honesty and simplicity are what is needed in bed, and you can help her get in touch with her true feelings by making her feel accepted for what she is. You should keep an open mind, and encourage her to do the same, because there is not one 'standard' response that she should achieve.

Homosexuality

Human sexuality is a complex phenomenon, and not so neatly categorized by the labels 'heterosexual' and 'homosexual' as society could wish. Between the strong and exclusive attraction of man to woman, and that of man to man, or woman to woman, lies a whole spectrum of sexual and emotional affinities: the ardour, or warmth, or coolness of any human relationship depends on the individuals within it, and not on any of the arbitrary specifications which might be imposed by society.

Some men want sex with other men as a permanent part of their lives; some are curious about male bodies, and may experiment at some time in their lives; some feel equally attracted to men and to women; some men enjoy looking at other men's bodies without desiring sexual contact; some prefer the company of other men for leisure; some work in an all-male environment. Women also feel and do all these things with other women. These infinite permutations and the confusion that results from them cannot be accommodated by society, which needs order in which to function. Order means ignoring varying shades of grey and distinguishing only between black and white; it means putting labels on things. And since society is never stronger than when it is united against a common evil, labelling things also means defining society's outcasts.

Various attempts have been made this century to 'explain' homosexuality, and even to 'cure' it. But the question is not really why some people are homosexual, but why our society is heterosexual. People born into a homosexual society generally conform to the norm, just as do people born into a heterosexual society. Most of us have a broad enough sexual response to allow us to be conditioned comfortably to either mode of behaviour. The people who feel less comfortable with the status quo, and those who feel positive discomfort with it are in no way unnatural; rather, it is the restrictions that society places on them that should be considered against nature.

One man in three has had some form of homosexual experience resulting in orgasm, according to the Kinsey Report, published in 1948. Kinsey was not saying that one man in three was homosexual; but he was tearing off the label that branded sexuality between men as 'abnormal'. Kinsey pointed out that humans were not alone among animals in engaging in same-sex activity: the assumption that animals had sex only when reproduction could be guaranteed was a man-made one, designed to bolster the view that homosexuality was 'against nature'. Of course, half a century has elapsed since the publication of the Kinsey Report and sexual mores have changed. However, Kinsey's findings still represent extremely valuable research into this area of sexual behaviour and the underlying trends are still relevant today.

Homosexual encounters between men usually begin in foreplay and end in orgasm, but the pattern of lovemaking is much less rigid than the pattern of lovemaking between men and women tends to be, and both partners almost always reach orgasm. Many homosexual men consider sex with other men to be liberating because there are no rules: it does not involve pressure to perform or pressure to satisfy the other person, and mutual satisfaction is effortless because men understand each other's bodies so well.

Men report that another advantage of sex without obligations is that they feel they can come straight to the point; a sexual relationship often precedes a social friendship, and not the other way around. Many men describe their sexual relations with male partners as generally more honest and straightforward, both physically and emotionally, than their relationships with women.

Most homosexual men derive a great deal of physical and emotional satisfaction from being penetrated. Hygiene should always be the first priority in any act of anal penetration, as disease is especially easily transmitted in this way. Always wear a condom. A condom on a finger inserted into the anus can aid lubrication as well as protect against scratches – from fingernails and rough skin – that could lead to infection. You should always wash thoroughly before and after anal sex, and if you use a vibrator for penetration, make sure that this is washed thoroughly too, in hot soapy water with a splash of antiseptic added.

Some women rebel against the narrowness of the status quo and become lesbians for political reasons, feeling dissatisfied with a male-dominated society; others do so because they find men unsatisfactory as lovers or as partners on an emotional level; and others because they are intensely emotionally involved with a member of their own sex and wish to express their feelings through their sexuality.

Jealousy

It's only natural to want our partners to put us first, and we all have a limit to the amount of attention we can tolerate them paying to other men and women. But all too often, a flicker of jealousy flares up into a raging fire. Jealousy feeds on itself and grows into a disease that pollutes a relationship, and can cripple and destroy it. The jealous person rarely realizes that jealousy is of his or her own making, and that there is always a way out. The way out is to stop being a victim and take control. If you are jealous because your partner is having an affair, you have the option of removing yourself from the situation. But if you feel jealous when your partner so much as looks at someone else, then you need to re-evaluate the way you feel about yourself. It will help when you understand that jealousy is a habit, a trick of the mind that it's possible to unlearn.

The first step towards unlearning jealousy is to realize that your survival does not depend on your partner. Yes, of course he is unique and irreplaceable as a person, but he is not irreplaceable as a partner. And your existence does not depend on whether he loves you. There is no need to behave as though he has the power to turn off your life-support machine. You and you alone have the power of nourishing yourself by investing belief in your enduring worth.

The second step towards unlearning jealousy is to start believing in your enduring worth. Because they so lack confidence in their own worth, jealous people always believe that the hub of the universe is elsewhere. If you see your partner talking to another woman, you instantly assume that their conversation is more interesting than any you might have with him. You imagine that he must find the other woman more beautiful and fascinating than he finds you. Instantly, you perceive your partner as polarized on this paragon of desirability, while you yourself pale into emptiness. Don't be so quick to devalue yourself. How could you become less just because someone else has walked into the room? The hub of your universe lies within you, and it will continue to do so all your life. Your life force is what your partner relates to. The dynamics of your relationship are between the two of you, and in your power as much as his.

The third step is to be aware of your power. The jealous person presents herself as a victim of her partner's bad behaviour. The status of victim is demeaning. It says: 'I am not in control of my life; someone else is. I have no power to act; I let things be done to me.' This is nonsense: we all have the power to act. You need to break the cycle and take control. Instead of mutely accepting that you are dependent on your partner's approval, concentrate on the power of approval you have within you to give him. Instead of acting negatively, nagging and complaining, try acting positively, by letting your partner know in what ways and how much you appreciate him. Reinforcing the positive aspects of your relationship will do you both the power of good. If you are no longer attacking him, worrying him with your suspicions, he can let down his defences and start enjoying your company again. And you will feel good because you have relaxed the tension and taken the power of approval into your own hands.

The fourth step is to take equal responsibility for your relationship. When you start thinking of yourself as whole and powerful, you will feel the need to cling slipping gradually away. When you begin to see yourself as not inferior but equal, you can stop acting as your partner's keeper. When you realize you have the power to give, you will start to feel generous. Now you can give your partner the freedom your jealousy was denying him. You will be able to allow him to enjoy socializing with other people, secure in the knowledge that this will not affect the way he feels about you or threaten your relationship. And by centring your power within yourself and standing apart from him, you will have given him the freedom to come to you.

Infidelity

'Marriage is a great institution. But who wants to live in an institution?' This comment, made by Groucho Marx, reflects the ambiguity that people sometimes feel about monogamy.

A recent survey revealed that 70 per cent of married people have had extramarital sex. The most frequent reason given for this was that sex at home had become boring or non-existent. People have extramarital affairs because intimacy, eroticism and adventure have gone from their marriages. For the most part, they do not tell their partners, for fear of guilt and recrimination rocking the boat, and possibly breaking up the marriage. Affairs are sallies into the outside world of freedom, where married men and women can prove to themselves their sexual potency and desirability, and enjoy a secret act of revenge on their partner, with whom they no longer feel either potent or desirable.

Involvement with other people can sometimes lead to the realization that so much is lacking in the marriage that it is unsalvageable, but most extramarital affairs do not pose a real threat to the institution. Some people use affairs to 'keep themselves going' in a marriage that has worn thin, but whose commitments seem inescapable; others see their extramarital experience simply as a secret enrichment of their own lives – a token 'independence'.

The attraction of an affair is that it holds the promise of an experience that is the exact opposite of marriage. There are no social responsibilities to cripple the lovers' attitudes to one another or inhibit their sexuality; and the limited time available for encounters heightens emotional urgency. In this atmosphere, intimacy and good sex thrive.

An affair is unlikely to happen in a relationship that is kept flexible. Don't let your individuality disappear underneath your married role, and don't take your partner for granted. It is important to maintain a discussion of your roles and responsibilities towards each other, and to experiment with different arrangements so that you don't get stale and build up resentments. Frequent open discussion of every aspect of your relationship will break down barriers between you, thereby creating deeper understanding and bringing you closer together.

Infidelity

Sex in pregnancy

Unless you are told otherwise by your doctor, it is perfectly safe for you to have sex throughout your pregnancy. However, towards the expected birth date, your size may make many positions uncomfortable for you. Penetration may be easiest if you lie on your side and your partner enters from behind. Oral sex and mutual masturbation should cause no problems. Some women fear that sexual activity or orgasm may trigger off labour, but sex cannot induce labour unless the baby is due anyway, when the prostaglandins present in the man's semen may cause it to start.

The sex drive of some women decreases during the first trimester of pregnancy. This may be due to tiredness and nausea, or to a hidden belief that it is 'not right' for a mother to enjoy sex. The problem will usually disappear of its own accord. In some women, the sex drive actually increases during the middle three months (the second trimester) of pregnancy, and some claim that their lovemaking is more satisfying than ever before. This may be because the high level of circulating hormones means that a woman can be stimulated more easily and reach a pitch of sexual excitement more quickly than when not pregnant. A pregnant woman's sexual organs – breasts, nipples and genitals – are especially highly developed, which probably increases sexual awareness. Finally, there is of course complete freedom from the worry of getting pregnant, which allows a deeper level of 'letting go'.

Some women and their partners worry that sex may harm the unborn child, but such fears are groundless. The foetus is protected from infection by the plug of mucus at the neck of the womb. In rare cases, infection can occur, but this is usually due to lack of normal hygiene precautions or having sex with several different partners. The baby is also protected against being squashed by the amniotic fluid in which it floats in the womb. Avoid over-athlectic sex because it will be uncomfortable for you, but don't worry about hurting the baby. Sex should not cause a miscarriage in a normal, healthy pregnancy.

You can resume sex after childbirth as soon as it is comfortable to do so. Women who have had an episiotomy (in which the perineum is cut to facilitate birth), will probably feel sore for at least three weeks. When you feel confident that your wound has healed, begin to re-establish your sex life,

taking it slowly and gently and using a lubricating jelly if necessary to prevent scar tissue causing discomfort or pain. It is important to establish sexual contact with your partner as soon as you can, as you will both need to get close again. If you still feel sore, remember there are other ways of giving and receiving affection. Don't let your partner feel that you are lavishing all your care and attention on your baby and excluding him from your love.

The following pages show three sex positions that may prove comfortable during the various stages of pregnancy.

Positions for pregnancy

Leapfrog
The woman kneels on the bed with legs spread wide, and falls comfortably forwards as the man enters her from behind. He can then caress her back and control the depth of thrust. This position is ideal when the woman starts to feel uncomfortable with the man's weight pressing down on her and she wants to protect her belly from over-enthusiastic thrusting.

Spoons
The woman lies comfortably on her side and the man enters her from behind, fitting his body closely to hers. This position puts no pressure on the woman's abdomen and is suitable for the most advanced stages of pregnancy. The man can cuddle up close and caress her breasts, while kissing her shoulders and the nape of her neck.

Astride

This is a good position for the middle months of pregnancy, when the missionary position has become uncomfortable, but the woman has quite a bit of energy for sex. She sits astride the man's lap and supports herself with her arms. He can help her as she moves up and down on top of him, taking control when she gets tired.

Sex and family life

Having a family shifts the emphasis of your relationship. Considering yourselves as parents first and partners second certainly makes for a stable home life and a secure environment in which your children can grow up, but what of your responsibility towards each other? When you do have a moment to yourselves, what do you talk about? Do you tap into each other's feelings like when your first met? Do you ask personal questions and get personal answers? Or does all your conversation revolve around your children, home improvements, career moves and family holidays? Do you feel that the individuals you once were have become completely saturated in the roles of parent, partner and householder?

Family life can completely drown out intimacy unless you work very hard to maintain a sense of your own and each other's individuality. A teething baby crying in the night, a small child who creeps in to share your bed, older children who get up early and stay up late: it's easy to see how partners come to regard themselves and each other as parents rather than as lovers.

In order to stay lovers and friends, parents need to keep time for themselves, right from the start. This means being firm about your right to privacy. Don't allow small babies and toddlers to dominate your evenings: try to get them used to regular bedtimes. Make sure your children go to bed at the same time each evening, even if they don't go to sleep straight away but lie in bed reading or play quietly in their rooms. Explain to them that you all need private time in which to relax.

As your children grow, teach them the value of privacy. This is best done by showing them the courtesies and consideration you wish for yourselves. If you want your bedroom to be your private zone, they will be more willing to respect your wishes if you treat them equally, by not walking into their rooms unannounced or rummaging through their personal belongings without permission. Giving teenagers time and space in which to pursue their own interests will make them more understanding of your need for some quiet while you read a book or listen to the radio.

Make sure your own parents, on both sides, also respect your right to privacy. Sometimes it can be difficult keeping over-intrusive relations and in-laws at bay without hurting either their feelings or those of your partner, but unless you are pleasantly firm, they can take over. Agree with your partner on a joint approach – third parties have a habit of driving a wedge between partners who differ.

The solution can be to try and put grandparents' energy and interest to positive use. Get them to look after their grandchildren, preferably in their own homes, so the two of you can have time to yourselves, and everyone will be happy. Don't let them spoil the children, though; put your foot down about sweets and other treats: they should not undermine your authority with over-indulgence.

Neighbours can also pose a threat to your privacy, if you let them. As with parents and in-laws, neighbours who 'pop in' and then can't be got rid of are liable to cause considerable tension between the partner who listens politely and the partner who is unable to hide frustration and resentment and takes noisy refuge in the other room. Tell your neighbour that a visit right now is not convenient and suggest a time when you can visit her at her house instead; then you can decide when it's time to come home.

Sharing private time with your partner can be a particularly sensitive issue if the children of his or her previous marriage are living with you, as jealousy and resentment can easily result if you seem to be claiming your partner's attention at their expense.

Keeping love alive

Healthy relationships are based on mutual liking, caring and sexual attraction. If these three vital elements cease to be felt and expressed, the life blood of the relationship dries up and just the empty shell remains. The couple may go on saying 'I love you' out of habit, but it now means little more than 'I am used to you.'

Many couples slip from passion to tolerance over the years because they don't bother to affirm their feelings for each other. Marriage can make people lazy. Promising to love each other for ever is not a guarantee that this will happen. Ask yourself what you mean by love. Do you like your partner? Do you care for him? Does he turn you on?

It's difficult to love someone you don't like. And it's difficult not to like someone whose company you enjoy. Make sure you don't give up the things you enjoyed doing together at the beginning. Your shared interests will keep you close. The only shared interest some couples have is watching television. Television can dominate your home and numb your emotional life by making it impossible to talk to one another. Sitting in front of the television night after night is a way of giving up responsibility towards your partner.

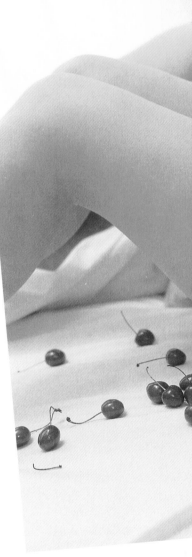

Find another interest in which you can both participate more actively. Above all, talk to each other and make each other laugh. The evening meal forms the focal point of most couples' days: sharing the planning, cooking and eating of it offers a good opportunity to appreciate each other's talent, fortitude and sense of humour.

Accept that your feelings towards your partner are a living force that fluctuates according to your moods and actions, and that sometimes you may like him to a pitch of delight, and at other times less. Whenever you really like your partner, make sure you tell him so. It's refreshing and realistic to be told: 'I do like you so much,' or 'You are so funny.' Such positive and specific comments often give a bigger boost to the ego than being told 'I love you.'

Encourage your partner to share problems with you, and in turn be open about the issues that are worrying you. You can't be expected to understand the minutiae of each other's situation at work, but professional and even technical problems all have a human angle that may be more obvious to the eye of the one who is not immersed in them. Just the act of explaining your problem to someone who listens with a sympathetic ear will lessen the burden and draw you closer together.

Caring for each other is often a practical thing. Remembering that you're performing chores in order to create an environment in which you can be happy together can take the drudgery out of them; if it doesn't, question their necessity, or at least the thoroughness and regularity with which you perform them. Creative caring means pulling off the blinkers of routine and being aware of your partner's fluctuations of mood. It's being able to drop what you're doing to lend a helping hand, or give advice, or a shoulder to cry on, or just a smile of wry understanding, in the knowledge that your partner will also be available for you.

Erotic techniques

Passionate sex between lovers can be made even more exciting by the cultivation of erotic techniques. Exploring your own and your partner's responses is a sexual adventure that opens the way to a deeper and more thrilling level of intimacy.

Kissing

There is an infinite variety of kisses that lovers can exchange, from playful or tender lip kissing to deeply arousing open-mouth kissing with tongue play. Kissing someone you are mad about is one of life's great pleasures – or should be. Surprisingly large numbers of people have no idea how to kiss, and a poor kisser can be a terrible disappointment, just as someone who is a skilled practitioner of the art of kissing can have you tearing off your clothes.

The lovers' kiss or French kiss, involving the whole mouth and tongue, is said to have its origins in the way mothers used to feed their babies in prehistoric cultures. This practice can be observed in peasant communities in some parts of Europe even today. The mother chews the food for her baby before transferring it directly from mouth to mouth. She pushes her tongue, and the food, inside the infant's mouth, and it reacts with searching movements of its tongue inside her mouth. Considerations of hygiene and today's associations of mouth-to-mouth contact with sexual arousal make this type of feeding unacceptable in our society, but the action lives on in adult erotic behaviour.

A deep kiss is very often the first mutual acknowledgement that sexual attraction exists between a couple, and it is the first element of sexuality to disappear from a relationship that is on the wane. According to Relate (the British Marriage Guidance Bureau), couples whose marriages are in trouble are more likely to have intercourse than to kiss. That mouth and tongue contact retain a special intimacy while intercourse can seem businesslike and remote is also illustrated by the fact that prostitutes never kiss their clients.

The first thing to do when kissing a new lover is to find out with your lips and tongue where his or her teeth are, so you can avoid banging into them with your own teeth. Clashing teeth is as impersonal as clashing spectacle frames. The next thing to remember is that kissing should be wildly exciting: don't get stuck in a rut endlessly repeating the same movement, or your partner will lose concentration and grow bored. Vary the pace, and vary the initiative, sometimes taking it, sometimes being receptive to your partner.

Erotic techniques

Here are a few tips for more enjoyable kissing:

- If your new partner does not smoke and you do, now would be a very good time to give up the habit. Non-smokers do not like the taste or smell of tobacco.

- Until you have got to know someone well and they have assured you they don't mind it, don't eat strong tasting food, such as garlic or curry, unless your lover is eating it too.

- Oral hygiene is important. Make sure your mouth looks and tastes good. Get your dentist to descale your teeth regularly and eat a healthy diet so that your breath is fresh.

- Don't kiss or have oral sex if you have a mouth or throat infection. Kissing can transfer an estimated 250 different bacteria and viruses carried in saliva, though as yet there is no evidence to suggest that AIDS can be caught in this way.

- Being kissed passionately by a man with a stubbly chin is not anywhere near as erotic as being kissed passionately by a man who has recently shaved.

- If you have a beard, consider the fact that it makes a barrier between your skin and your lover's. There is no doubt that more erotic contact is possible between a clean-shaven man and his partner.

- Women who wear make-up should be prepared to have it licked off or, at the very least, smudged. Consider how you feel about this before applying your make-up, but whatever you do, don't let yourself be inhibited by a perfectly painted face. Many men would prefer to kiss a face bare of make-up anyway.

- To maximize sensation when kissing, make full use of all the muscles in your mouth and tongue. It is much better kissing someone whose mouth responds to yours and who knows how to use pressure, than someone whose mouth is flabby and slack.

- Remember that nothing, but nothing, is worse than a slobbery kiss.

Masturbation

Masturbation is a natural and healthy method of sexual release engaged in by most people of both sexes. It is also a good way of learning one's own sexual response. Women who can bring themselves to orgasm by masturbating are more likely to have orgasms with their partners, and men who can masturbate for 15-20 minutes without ejaculating are less likely to suffer from problems of premature ejaculation during intercourse. Stimulating your partner's genitals is also called masturbation, and is an important part of lovemaking.

The external female genitals

are called the vulva. Pubic hair grows on the labia majora, and inside these outer vaginal lips are the labia minora, which are pinker and moister. If the sight of your own genitals is not familiar to you, examine them in a hand mirror while you relax after a bath or shower. The clitoris is situated where the labia minora join at the top. It is a pink knob about the size of a dried pea, and is highly sensitive. The clitoris is protected by a hood, which retracts during sexual arousal. Below the clitoris is the tiny opening of the urethra, through which urine passes, and below that is the opening to the vagina.

When you start to masturbate,

make sure you have plenty of time during which you won't be interrupted. Go somewhere where it is quiet, completely private, and warm. Some women like to lie on their back, some on their front; some like their legs pressed tightly together, others like them spread wide apart, or

propped up above the body. Use a lubricant and stroke yourself gently, with your fingers or an object such as a vibrator, varying your movements from time to time to find out where and how you like to be stimulated.

Many women find the clitoris too sensitive for direct stimulation, so you could begin by rubbing the whole vulva, then gradually move inside with delicate fingers. Allow yourself to fantasize to increase arousal. Be patient, but if the pleasure wears off without you having had an orgasm then you should stop. Don't be disappointed with yourself, as it may take several sessions before you can relax enough to really let go.

When you feel a gathering tension in the vaginal area and a build-up of warmth, orgasm is on the way. Continue to stimulate yourself, as if you stop, these sensations will fade and it may be difficult to get them back again. The clitoris becomes increasingly sensitive as you proceed, whether you are stimulating it directly or not, and then orgasm breaks out with waves of vaginal contractions. Most women like some form of genital contact during orgasm: either continued stimulation or pressing or holding the vaginal area. Some like to insert a finger into the vagina as they come.

Most men are expert at giving themselves pleasure, but there's no harm in extra practice. A good way of finding out exactly how your genitals respond to stimulation is by soaping and gentle massage in the bath, allowing yourself to fantasize as you do so. Some men enjoy fondling their testicles, and some enjoy penetrating the anus with a finger. There are many different strokes you can use on the penis. If you are uncircumcized, you can draw the foreskin over the head of the penis and then pull it back down the shaft to get an erection; if you are circumcized, repeated squeezing round the shaft and letting go is usually effective. Then you can let your hand glide up and down the shaft in long slow movements, gradually building up speed and pressure. You may enjoy rubbing or tickling the glans of the penis, though for some men this is too sensitive. You may like gentle or firm pulling, stroking, squeezing and stretching. Try holding off ejaculation by varying the stroke when you become too excited, before finally letting go in orgasm.

Masturbation need not be something that you do only when you are alone. Many people find the sight of their partner masturbating highly erotic. It can also be very instructive to discover how your partner reaches orgasm alone, as this will be the best method for you to adopt when you are masturbating him or her. Masturbating with your partner will break down inhibitions and allow you to get even closer.

Masturbating your partner in the way he or she enjoys is an important part of lovemaking, and many women like being masturbated to orgasm before penetration. Both men and women need to learn how to handle each other's genitals with tenderness and sensitivity.

Oral sex

Oral sex begins with the first deep kiss, and continues with kisses all over the body, concentrating finally on the genitals. On the part of the giver it requires a degree of emotional involvement, because it must be done with patience, tenderness, sensitivity and mounting but controlled excitement if it is to be really good. Lovers who give oral sex reluctantly and without generosity or enjoyment make their partners feel guilty and selfish, and too tense and worried to relax and take pleasure themselves.

From the receiver, oral sex requires trust, and the confidence that comes with being made to feel desirable. In sex, as in other areas of life, it is often more difficult to receive generosity than to give it, but the person who succumbs completely to pleasure delivers himself or herself over to the lover, and this also gives a sense of wonderment.
It goes without saying that sexual hygiene is of prime importance for anyone who engages in oral sex.

Oral sex for women is called cunnilingus. For many women, cunnilingus is the most exciting of all the variations of sex, and a gentle and skilful lover should be able to make his partner come with his tongue more easily than in any other way. A strong slippery tongue can be used with precision on the clitoris without danger of causing any pain, unlike a finger.

Begin by kissing your partner's face and mouth, and then gradually work your way down her body, kissing and stroking her breasts, belly and inner thighs. Flick your tongue in light feathery kisses along the fleshy folds of the outer labia, smoothing away the pubic hair and then parting the labia gently with your fingers. Move very gradually inwards with your tongue. Vary your movements according to your partner's response. Try nuzzling, burrowing, thrusting with your tongue into her vagina, sucking, long delicate licks, short rapid flicking licks. She may not like her clitoris to be stimulated directly at first, so proceed tentatively until she is fully aroused.

Once she can trust you and feel confident that you like what you are doing, she will be able fully to let go in orgasm. Being 'on the spot', a man can get a special thrill from experiencing so directly the blissful effect he has on his partner, as well as from her vulnerability and trust.

Erotic techniques

Oral sex for men is called fellatio. The experience of having their penis sucked, licked and kissed is one that most men find intensely exciting. In some cases, there may be psychological barriers to overcome. Some men fear being bitten during oral sex. The woman should open her mouth as wide as possible, and close her lips, but not her teeth, over the penis. Using all the muscles in the lips and tongue will mean that the teeth should not come into contact with the penis at all.

Some women are worried that they may be choked during fellatio. The way to allay this fear is to remain in control: you are the one who should move while your partner lies still, so there is no possibility of his thrusting deep into your throat and making you gag. Some women find the idea of swallowing semen repugnant. Of course there is no need for you to do this if you do not wish to, but many women do enjoy having their partner ejaculate into their mouth.

Work your way down your partner's body, beginning with kissing his face and mouth and progressing to his genitals. Be very gentle, as they are highly sensitive to pain. There are many ways of stimulating the penis with your lips and tongue. You can lick all along the shaft with a delicate tongue, then use more pressure and press your open lips as well as your tongue against it as you rub them up and down towards the head. You can lick and kiss the frenulum – the sensitive place where the glans joins the shaft on the underside, which will be facing towards you if the man is lying on his back with an erection. You can take the head of the penis in your mouth and suck it, tickling it at the same time with your tongue, and you can move your lips as far down the shaft as is comfortable, and then move up and down, sucking and pressing with your lips and tongue.

The '69' position is so called because the figures resemble a couple giving each other oral sex. While many couples find this a good way of arousing each other, others find it difficult to concentrate on giving and receiving such intense pleasure at the same time. If you are about to come in this position, it is best to break off from pleasuring your partner to avoid inadvertently biting him or her. Use your fingers to indicate to your partner what is happening and let yourself go in orgasm.

Massage and the art of touch

Rythmically stroking another person to bring relaxation and comfort is the oldest and simplest form of therapy in the world. Massage relieves nervous tension and relaxes knotted muscles, improving circulation and body tone and inducing a feeling of wellbeing and wholeness. In an intimate relationship, massage can flood into tender and erotic feelings, or send your partner drifting into a peaceful and rejuvenating sleep. You can use it to heal and soothe if you are tired or suffering from aching limbs, or to clear and concentrate the mind and relax the body if you are wide awake but as yet too tense and distracted to make love. Massage can be as beneficial for the giver as for the receiver if both parties concentrate themselves solely on the point of contact.

The requirements for massage are simple. You will need a warm quiet room. The atmosphere should be relaxing, the light dim; perhaps candlelight or firelight. You both need to be comfortable. The receiver should lie on a towel on a firm surface, such as the floor or your bed. To give a massage you should stand, sit or kneel in a balanced position, as any awkwardness or tension will transmit directly to your partner, as well as bothering you. A massage oil or cream will enable your hands to glide smoothly over your partner's body. Warm it before use by rubbing it between your palms; never drip it directly on to your partner's body. Take off all your jewellery and make sure that your nails are short and not sharp.

Essential preparation for giving a massage is to centre yourself. The Japanese have a word, *hara*, which means lower abdomen. They believe that this is the centre of the body, from which power flows. Focus yourself on this centre and allow the power to spread through your body until it reaches your arms and fingertips. Relax your hands and wrists by shaking them. While you are massaging your partner, keep your back straight and move from your pelvis. Always keep yourself aware of the power in your hands.

The next pages show a simple massage sequence. Feel free to adapt it to your own mood and requirements.

The back

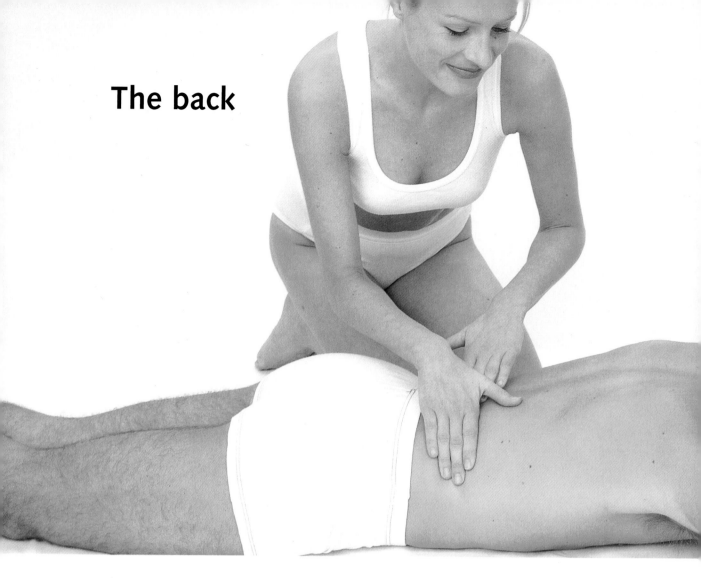

ONE Start on the side of the body opposite you. Work from the small of the back, massaging down the sides and up to the shoulder blades.

Erotic techniques

TWO Work around the shoulder blade with the whole hand, pushing away from the spine with firm strokes.

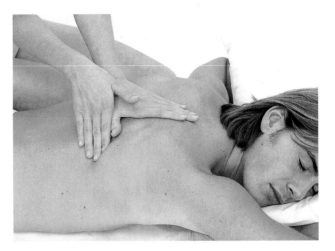

THREE Pull the muscle towards you with your fingertips and circle under the shoulder blade with the flat of your hand.

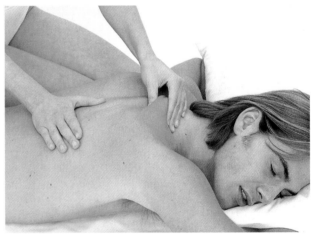

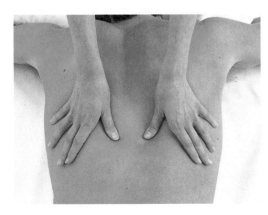

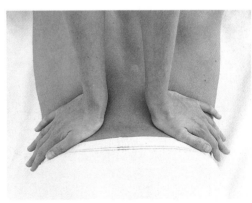

FOUR Position yourself at the top of your partner's head and with thumbs on either side of the spine (not on the spine, on the muscle), work down towards the buttocks with small circular movements.

FIVE Smooth down the back with the flat of the hand, being careful to avoid the spine.

Back of legs and ankles

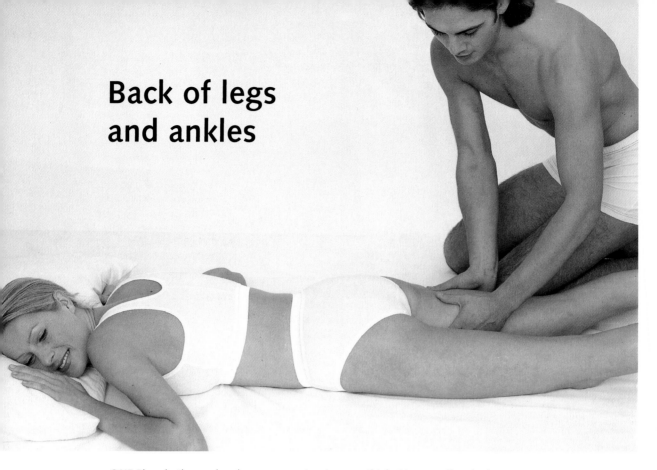

ONE Place both your hands on your partner's upper thigh. Use your thumbs to massage down the leg in small outward circles from the thigh down to the ankle, working on all the muscles as you go.

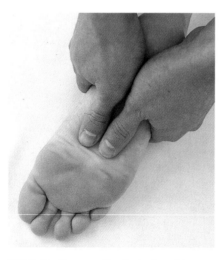

TWO Continue on the foot, describing small outward spiralling circles. Press firmly enough not to tickle.

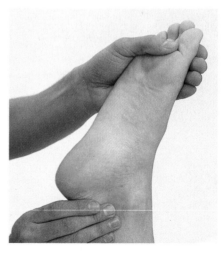

THREE Bend the leg at the knee joint and stretch the foot carefully upwards. Rotate the ankle slowly and gently, first in one direction, then the other.

Erotic techniques

FOUR Gently lift the leg and move it slowly from side to side. Do not force it. Stop if your partner feels uncomfortable.

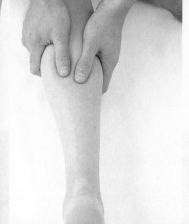

FIVE Lower the leg and finish with long firm strokes from thigh to ankle.

Shoulders, arms and hands

ONE Your partner now lies on her back. Hold the hand nearest you and massage the muscle between the shoulder and neck with your thumb.

TWO Work with your thumb all the way down the front of the arm to the hand. Repeat down the back of the arm.

THREE Massage the hand and fingers with tiny circular thumb movements. Gently stretch and rotate the fingers, first in one direction, then in the other.

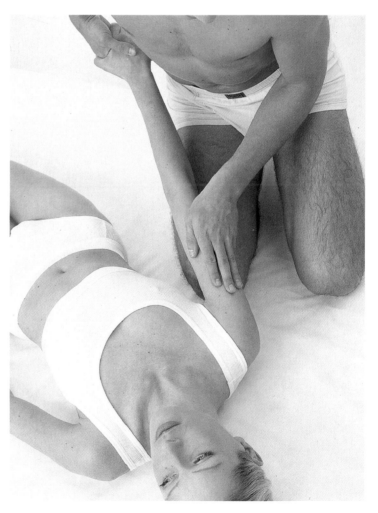

FOUR Finish with long firm strokes from the shoulder to the fingers.

Chest and abdomen

ONE Massage the chest muscles below the collar bone with your thumb.

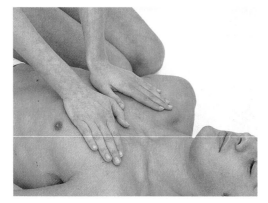

TWO Circulate with the flat of your hand round the breast and rib area.

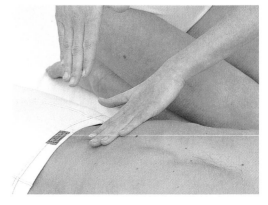

THREE Again with the flat of the hand, pull diagonally across the abdomen.

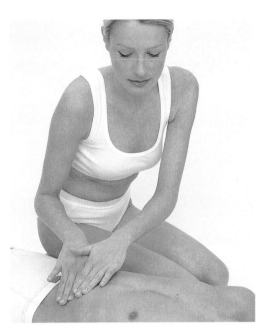

FOUR Make gentle circular strokes on your partner's abdomen with your fingertips. Work outwards and clockwise.

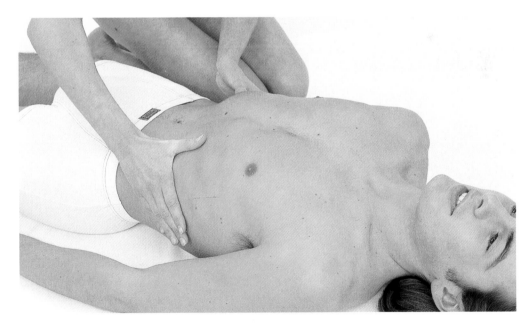

FIVE To finish, hold your partner's sides firmly and gently while he breathes deeply in and out.

Front of legs and feet

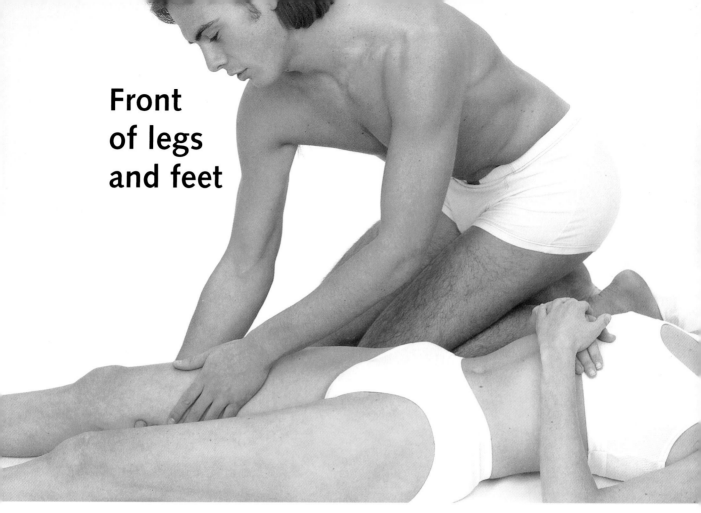

ONE Support the back of your partner's knee with one hand. Follow the contour of the thigh muscle with the thumb of your other hand, working in a diagonal from the inside of the knee to the hip.

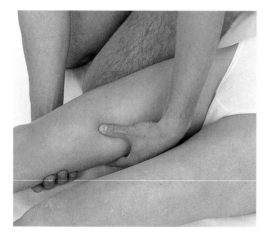

TWO With your thumb, work on the muscle of the outer thigh in small circular movements. Repeat on the inner thigh.

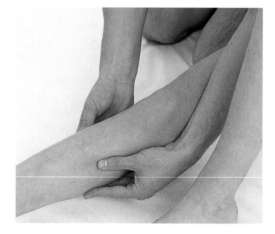

THREE Using both hands, massage down the calf muscle with circular thumb movements and all the way down to the foot on both sides of the leg.

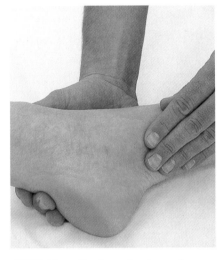

FOUR Move the fingertips in small circles round the ankle bone.

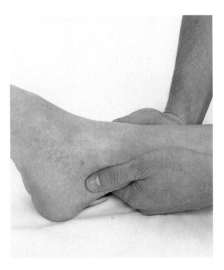

FIVE Massage the inner heel with rotating thumb movements on each side of the foot.

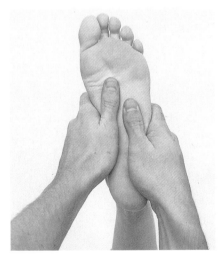

SIX Massage the sole of the foot with your thumb, pressing firmly. Work upwards to the toes.

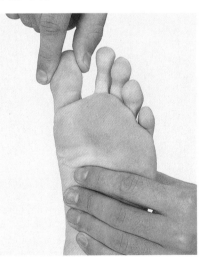

SEVEN Stretch each toe and rotate it gently, first in one direction, then the other.

Neck, head and face

ONE Position yourself at the top of your partner's head and push down firmly but gently on the shoulders with the heels of your hands.

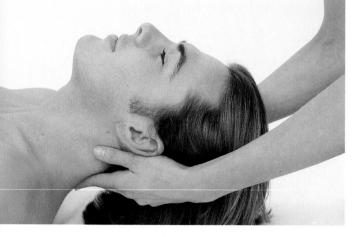

TWO Lift your partner's head and gently stretch his neck. Position his head with chin up so you can get your hands behind his neck. Massage the back of his neck with your fingertips.

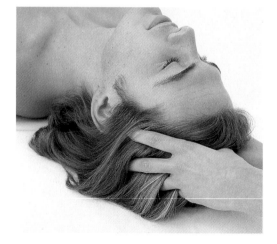

THREE Work over the scalp with the fingertips of both hands, as if you were washing his hair.

Erotic techniques

FOUR Rest your hands on your partner's forehead while he breathes deeply.

FIVE Smooth your thumbs to the centre of the brow and away again several times, moving with your partner's breathing.

SIX Circulate your thumbs on the temples in small gentle movements.

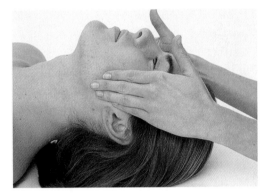

SEVEN Gently smooth the flesh of the face upwards and outwards from cheek to chin with your fingertips.

EIGHT Lift the head and stretch the neck again, turning the head gently from one side to the other.

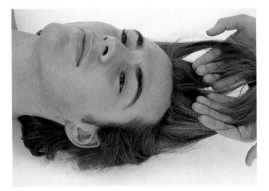

NINE Finish by pulling your fingers gently upwards through his hair.

Sex positions

The missionary is the most commonly adopted lovemaking position, because it is so comfortable, but there are many different ways of enjoying each other's bodies, and each of the positions illustrated on the next pages may suggest another into which you can move.

Greater intimacy is offered by some positions, with all-over body contact and the opportunity to embrace and kiss; others offer deeper penetration; some are quite difficult to maintain, which creates a certain sense of urgency and excitement.

Adventurous lovers will find variations of their own, either by design or by chance: you may get overtaken by lust half way up the stairs or while talking in the kitchen. The important thing is to engage all your instincts and feelings, while remaining acutely aware of your partner's responses.

Split level

This is one of a number of 'split-level' positions that
gives the partners a different view of each other
and a different angle of penetration.
Here, the woman lies on her back, her legs round her
partner's waist, while he kneels. He is in total control,
and can also stimulate her clitoris with his fingers.
From this position he can let her legs drop and lie on top of her
in the missionary position, or he can raise her legs, resting them
around his shoulders, then bend forward to kiss her mouth
at the same time gaining depth of penetration.

Erotic techniques

Fireside

In this cosy position, which can follow cunnilingus, the woman
sits comfortably in an armchair with her hands and legs around
the man, who enters kneeling in front of her. If she leans back,
he can support himself with his hands on the back of the chair,
which will allow him more thrust.

Futon

For this position you need to try out all your furniture
to find a piece of the correct height. The woman lies on the
edge of a table, futon or bed covered with quilts and pillows,
and spreads her legs wide. The man can begin by kneeling to
give her cunnilingus, then he enters her, supporting himself
on his knees and holding her legs.
This affords him a great deal of control,
and the angle of penetration is steep.

Swimming

The man lies on his back, spreading his legs, and his partner lies on top of him, her legs along his, her feet on his. There is a good opportunity for kissing and total body contact. She controls the pace of lovemaking by dragging herself up and down against him. Many women find this position very exciting and are more likely to reach orgasm without direct clitoral stimulation this way than any other.

She can vary the position by closing her legs tight while his remain spread, or by getting him to close his, or both. She can also move easily from this position to sit up facing him.

Spreadeagle

In this rear entry position, the woman lies face down with the
man on top of her. She spreads her legs and he supports his
weight on his arms. If she raises her bottom off the bed slightly,
perhaps with the aid of a pillow under her hips, then it
will be possible to achieve deeper penetration.
The man can also lie with his full weight on his partner,
from which position it is easy to roll into 'spoons'.

Crawl

Deep penetration can be achieved with the woman on all fours and her partner kneeling behind her. This position gives both lovers the opportunity to thrust against one another, and the man may also caress his partner's breasts, buttocks and clitoris. Rear entry positions like this one are ideal when both partners are in the mood for vigorous rather than tender lovemaking. A variation is for both partners to stand with the woman bending forward and supporting herself against furniture.

Lap

This is a position that may suggest itself while cuddling on the
sofa. The man sits with the woman straddling his lap, facing
him. She controls the pace, they can kiss and he can caress her
breasts. She moves up and down on him, supporting herself
with her knees on the sofa, and her arms around his neck.
If they use a dining chair, she can keep her feet on the floor and
hold on to the chair back for support if necessary. If she faces
away from him, they will be able to achieve deeper penetration,
and she could support herself against furniture in front of her.

Head to toe

The man lies on his back with his legs spread and his penis inside
the woman, who also lies down on her back, with her legs
spread across his, her toes pointing to his head, and her head
away from him. The woman is in control.
The partners cannot see each other and sensation
is concentrated on the genitals.
This position can be adopted from one in which the lovers sit on
the bedfacing one another, their legs interlaced.

Erotic techniques

Missionary

The missionary position is the most popular lovemaking position of all because it is comfortable, affords a great deal of body contact and good depth of penetration. The lovers can kiss and hold each other at the same time. The woman lies on her back with her legs spread and her knees raised, and her partner lies on top between her legs.

From this position the woman can move to clasp her legs behind her partner's back or to close them tightly underneath him, while he spreads his.

Fellatio

In fellatio, the woman sucks, licks, kisses and strokes her
partner's penis. Exquisitely satisfying for the man, fellatio can
also give enormous erotic pleasure to the woman as she senses
his responses and his total abandonment to her.

Erotic techniques

Cunnilingus

In cunnilingus, the man stimulates his partner's vulva and clitoris with his lips and tongue. For most women, cunnilingus gives the most delicious sensual pleasure and is the best way of climaxing. It is also extremely arousing for her partner.

Erotic techniques

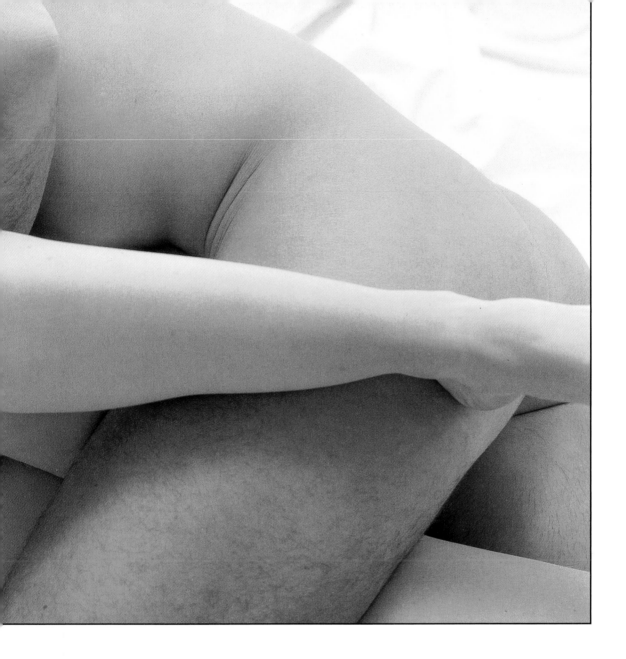

Cuissade

This position is known as 'cuissade', from the French *cuisse*, meaning thigh. The woman lies on her back, with the man at her side. She raises the leg nearest to him and rests it on his body, and he enters from under her thigh, with his nearest leg crossing her body.
They can hold one another and kiss, and the position is a very intimate one, possibly because of the 'secretive' form of entry.
The woman can exert a certain amount of restraint with her thigh, which can make it more exciting.

Standing carry

The man stands, holding his partner in his arms. She wraps her
legs round his waist and her arms round his shoulders. She can
move against him by pulling herself up and down, and he can
help her with his arms. This position can be assumed from
sitting. It can, of course, be adopted
in a very confined space, but it is quite strenuous.
From this position you can return to sitting, or the man can
gently lower his partner on to a bed or preferably a table, where
thrusting can continue without so much exertion.

Legs over

The woman lies on her back with her legs raised and wrapped
around the man's shoulders. He supports himself
on his arms above her. This position affords deep penetration,
and can be helped by placing a pillow under her buttocks. He
can lean forward to kiss her, and because her legs seem to be
pushing him away, though both her mouth
and vagina invite him, this is a position that can be very exciting.
If the woman's legs or the man's arms get too tired, the couple
can relax into the missionary position.

Standing

Both parties stand, using the wall as support. This position is
often used when the desire to make love strikes unexpectedly.
Part of the excitement lies in the fact that it is not easy
to move in this position.

Astride

With the man lying on his back on the bed, the woman
can sit astride him and control the pace of their lovemaking.
Facing him, she may squat on her haunches for a more powerful
bouncing movement, or, as here, kneel, supporting herself
with her hands. This way, she is free to lean forward
and kiss his mouth.
From this position it is easy for her to increase the intimacy
by lying with her whole body along his.
A variation is for her to face away from him, increasing
the depth of penetration.

Spoons

The 'spoons' position is so named because of the close fit
of the two bodies. The partners lie on their sides and the man
enters from behind. This position is cosy and relaxing, good for
slow drowsy lovemaking prior to falling asleep, or on
waking during the night.
It is also a comfortable position to adopt later in pregnancy
when most others put too much pressure on the woman's belly.

Erotic techniques

Urgent

This position is ideal for when you are unexpectedly
overtaken by the urge to make love. It does not require
more than a loosening of the clothes if you want.
The woman leans over the nearest available piece
of furniture and the man enters from behind.
It is good for fast exciting sex and gives both partners
the opportunity to thrust against one another.

Side by side

This position, with the lovers lying side by side and facing one another, is easy to slip into after mutual masturbation, and can be a prelude to rolling over with either partner on top. Here, the woman has her leg wrapped round her partner's body to facilitate deeper penetration: she pulls him towards her with her leg as he thrusts. The partners can kiss and touch each other's genitals while making love in this position.

Erotic techniques

Cross

Here the woman lies on her back on the bed and the man lies
diagonally across her. She opens her legs to allow him to enter
and he rocks gently from side to side. She can guide his
movements with the pressure of her hands. This position is
somewhat easier to maintain if the man lies beneath on his back
and the woman is in control.

Ringing the changes

Intercourse allows for all over, inside-and-outside closeness, and for a pair of lovers who are highly sensitized towards one another, it provides the most intimate form of communicating erotic love. Anyone who is enthusiastic about their partner will want to try other ways of expressing their love, and though spontaneous choice is more exciting than pre-planning, you can also get a lot of fun out of talking over your ideas.

Ringing the changes

Experimental sex

Introducing variety to your sex life can help to give your relationship a necessary boost. However, men and women often experiment with sex without love or involvement as part of their quest for real fulfillment. Some people imagine that experiences with prostitutes and partner-swapping are 'advanced' sex practices, whereas in fact they are just a substitute for good close one-to-one sex. People usually indulge in experiments out of boredom or desperation, or because of an inability to face the responsibility of mutual emotional involvement. However, boredom and desperation are felt by most people at some stage in their lives, and many are as curious to experiment with their sexuality as they are to discover their potential and learn their likes and dislikes in other areas.

The risks that go with sexual experimentation

are high. The more sexual partners you have, the greater the chance of catching VD and AIDS; for protection, men and women intent on experiment should always carry a packet of condoms. The emotional risks are not negligible either, and such encounters may often leave you feeling degraded and worthless, especially if you are a woman.

Prostitutes are often referred to as the members of

the world's 'oldest profession', and have been the butt of man's hatred for woman since time immemorial. The history of prostitution in Britain makes grim reading. Until the widespread use of the condom in the 1860s and '70s, prostitutes were regularly infected by their clients with syphilis and other venereal diseases, which they in turn passed on. They lived in increasing filth and degradation, often dying insane or blind after suffering terrible agonies, with alcohol as their only comfort. They were preached to by moralizing zealots, who were ignorant of the poverty and desperation that had turned them on to the streets; and they were subjected to brutal treatment, compulsory incarceration and examination by officers of the law, often under the eyes of jeering crowds. It has been suggested that the murders of Jack the Ripper were an act of revenge by a man who had contracted VD from a whore; this was certainly the motive of at least two other convicted multiple murderers whose targets were prostitutes.

The lives of today's prostitutes have benefited immeasurably from the advances which have been made in the prevention and cure of venereal disease. The profession thrives on clients who have an otherwise less than adequate sexual outlet, sometimes because the type of sexual gratification they crave is available nowhere else. Some prostitutes specialize in catering for men with sexual inhibitions that make them turn to sadism (in which sexual pleasure is gained from cruelty or abuse to another; named after the French writer, the Marquis de Sade, 1740–1814) or masochism (sexual pleasure gained from being physically abused; named after the Austrian novelist Leopold von Sacher-Masoch, 1835–1895). Indeed, prostitutes can command a high price for allowing such men to enact their fantasies.

Other men visit prostitutes for quick sexual relief either because they do not want to be bothered with the process of getting to know someone, which would cost both time and money, or because they are unable to form relationships. Sometimes adolescent boys visit a prostitute, either alone or goaded on by their mates, for their first sexual experience. In all cases, paying for sex has the advantage of being secret, anonymous, quick, free of the fear of rejection, and without any of the pressures of social or emotional involvement.

Having to pay for sex can make a man feel personally undesirable and therefore less masculine. Reducing sex to a business transaction with a woman means that there will be no warmth or affection and the woman will experience no pleasure herself. Many men feel degraded by the impersonality of the encounter, although this is exactly what others value, regarding it as just another professional service.

Swinging and swapping are terms used for experiments in which couples exchange partners, either within a group or within a foursome, and have sex, often in each other's presence. This type of sexual diversion was particularly popular among bored Americans before the advent of AIDS, and swingers' clubs, with bars, swimming pools, jacuzzis, saunas and rooms full of mattresses, operated quite openly. As well as the health risk, swingers face grave emotional danger.

Ringing the changes

Belonging and trust are inescapable elements of intimate sexual love, and people who claim not to be jealous are almost invariably kidding themselves. It can be a very destructive experience to witness your partner apparently enjoying sex with someone else, especially as the reason for swinging in the first place has to be that sex between you is pretty mediocre. The worst possible situation occurs when one of the partners is reluctant, and has gone along just to please the other in the hope of avoiding secret infidelity. Sex with people you don't know or care about can seem pointless and squalid, and sex with other couples whom you know and like can ruin friendships. To perform publicly an act that is naturally private can be sordid and degrading.

The aim of swinging is to introduce variety into a stale marriage, and by giving your partner permission to have sex with others under your supervision, to grant him or her a new measure of 'independence', while, at the same time, banishing jealousy. The same idea was behind the communes of the 1960s and '70s, which espoused 'free love' and 'open marriage'. Many of these communes disbanded when the relationships within them broke up under the strain of jealousy and guilt.

Psychiatrists who have studied open marriages and swinging partnerships report that tragic complications inevitably arise and lead to the ultimate breakdown of the relationship, which is usually entering its final phase when the experiments take place. If we were released from social conventions, no doubt we could share our partners without disastrous consequences, however, social conditioning makes it difficult for us to successfully participate in open relationships.

Freud put forward the theory that indiscriminate sexual activity used up the creative urge, which could otherwise be put to use for the benefit of society as a whole. While it is generally believed that a person who is sexually fulfilled in a strong relationship is better able to function than one who is repressed or thwarted, sexual self-restraint is not necessarily a bad thing. It can allow development in other areas of life.

Fantasy

The imagination enriches life by offering alternatives to reality. Sexual fantasy offers immediate gratification of desire without the complication and responsibility of involving other people. It is a substitute for the sexual experience that we are prevented from indulging in, either because of practicalities, or because we are inhibited by social or cultural taboos.

Dreams are a rich and sometimes surprising outlet for the sexual impulse. The dramatist and critic Kenneth Tynan composed an imaginary letter on this subject to The Times: 'Dear Sir, I hope I am not a prude, but I feel compelled to lodge a protest against the ever-increasing flood of obscenity in dreams. Many of my friends have been as shocked and sickened as myself by the filth that is poured out nightly as soon as our eyes are closed. It is certainly not my idea of "home entertainment". Night after night, the most disgraceful scenes of perversion and bestiality are perpetrated behind my eyelids… It is imperative that official action should be taken.' Dreams, even more so than waking fantasies, are free of the jurisdiction of the internal censor who 'takes official action' and regulates our social behaviour. But whereas we have no control over our dreams, we can guide our fantasies.

A sexual fantasy will always differ from the real-life enactment of the very same scene in one important particular: in the fantasy

everything can be controlled and run in perfect accordance with the fantasizer's wishes. The will of the other person or people does not intrude, and nor do extraneous physical sensations. For this reason, sexual fantasy can form the perfect accompaniment to masturbation, with the fantasizer concentrating on marrying the fluid mental picture with the exquisite sensations of building up to orgasm.

Private fantasy can also be used during intercourse as an aid to arousal and orgasm, and may prove an effective stimulus. The disadvantage is that it draws a veil between you and your partner and blocks out immediacy. Instead of concentrating on what you are experiencing, you float off in your imagination to where you may be having sex with the man next door, or an anonymous stranger. The alienation from your partner and from the present is such that you might just as well be masturbating alone.

If you usually fantasize during intercourse, you are missing out. You can put your imagination to better use by talking to your partner about what sensations you enjoy the most, and showing him or her how to give them to you. Get your partner to proceed very slowly and gently, continuing to give guidance or encouragement. Concentrate together on every exquisite sensation, emptying your mind of all thought, giving your body over to pure feeling. An orgasm achieved this way is truly shared.

Some lovers go one step further and tell each other their private fantasies. In an atmosphere of complete trust and acceptance, this can be highly erotic. It can break down inhibitions and increase the intimacy of both minds and bodies. For couples who are less close, there is a risk. Hearing that your partner fantasizes about your best friend, or about someone at work, can make you angry and upset unless you are confident that there is no desire to turn fantasy into reality. Talking about your fantasy can also make you feel very vulnerable, because fantasies are a flimsy protection against reality, and they cover our weak spots.

For both men and women, fantasies usually involve simply imagining basic sexual activities with their lovers, with other people they know, or with one or more total strangers, real or anonymous. The settings may be exotic or unusual, the props and clothes extravagant or bizarre, and the sexual prowess of the participants prodigious, but these features are just embellishments on a familiar theme.

The most common variations are fantasies that also involve elements of dominance and submission. Most people find something appealing in the idea of one partner being utterly at the tender mercy of the other. The submissive partner may be physically restrained in some way. This fantasy is probably so attractive because it recreates life's first loving experience of the mother ministering to the needs of the helpless baby. The passive partner relinquishes all responsibility, and is therefore 'permitted' to enjoy what happens in a totally selfish way; the active partner takes full control, and this role too offers selfish pleasure, albeit of a different sort.

Fantasies of dominance and submission deny the mutual participation of the one-to-one adult sex act and, in making the two roles opposite and distinct, free the participants from the responsibilities of closeness. These fantasies may be acted out by couples who are shy of intimacy, and the release brought by acknowledging the different needs of each partner may paradoxically bring the couple closer together. This explains the roots of fantasies of slavery and bondage, but why should anyone find spanking appealing?

The attraction of spanking probably lies in early childhood.

A child who has been spanked for playing with his or her genitals will associate genital arousal with an admonitory whack on the bottom. In time, the two sensations may become inseparable, and there are some people who find it impossible to orgasm without the stimulation of being spanked. The reason this happens more often to men than to women is that little boys' genitals are more accessible, and so they are more likely to fiddle with themselves and be caught doing so than little girls. Spanking, bondage and slavery are harmless ways of gaining sexual pleasure for those who wish to escape from the responsibility of the adult relationship into the irresponsibility of childhood.

Many fabrics have sex appeal.

The fabric forms a barrier between the lover and the loved one's body, and this has the tantalizing effect of heightening desire, while at the same time offering protection against the demands of naked intimacy. Leather is associated with bondage, hence its thrill. Silk is valued for its smoothness, and its transparency when wet; fur for its resemblance to pubic hair; and rubber for its ability to cling to the figure. When wet, the feel of rubber resembles that of the body's inner skin.

Fantasies of violence and rape give pleasure to some men,

and usually end unrealistically with the woman enjoying the experience. This sort of fantasy probably reflects massive frustration with a lack of meaningful and close relationships. Failure to establish intimacy by normal interaction can trigger the desire to 'smash and grab' for it, to batter down the barriers and snatch the prize. In his imagination the man is rewarded for violence by the pleasure of his partner. The implication is that he lacks the confidence to believe that his partner could completely desire him in reality. Though few men would wish to translate this violent fantasy into reality, it does explain why men are not prompted to rape in real life out of lust – they can achieve orgasm easily through masturbation – but out of anger with women, and out of a lack of self-esteem. When love is thwarted, it can come out as violence.

Water play

Water is the most therapeutic of elements: its buoyancy lifts the spirits and its all-over embrace gives freedom to body and mind. Having a bath together is a great way to relax before making love. When sharing a bath, make the mood luxurious by lighting candles and scenting the room with a sensual essential oil in an oil burner. Jasmine, ylang-ylang and rose are both soothing and stimulating. Gentle music turned down low and a deep tub full of warm water piled with your favourite bubbles will help wash away the tensions of the day along with dirt and grime.

Revitalizing weekends splashing about at a health spa allow some couples to get away from it all to enjoy facials, mudbaths, saunas, seaweed treatments, whirlpools and steam therapies, but you can pamper your partner with some of these treats inexpensively at home.

The Japanese practice of taking a hot bath followed by a brisk cold shower can give a tingling feeling of all-over vitality. Or, while your partner sits in a bath perfumed with oil of basil (good for headaches, anxiety, depression and fatigue), make him a face pack of avocado mashed with a little olive oil (you can lick it off afterwards), and put cooling slices of cucumber on his eyes. Try a seaweed body mask (many seaweed products are available commerically) followed by a long soak, then a refreshing shower and a brisk towel massage. Wrap him in a thick warm towel, then use another to rub him dry from ankles up to buttocks and hands to shoulders. Dry his back by holding a towel behind him and pulling on it from side to side, and pat any remaining damp skin gently dry.

Another way to enjoy water together is to shampoo your partner's hair. Wet the hair thoroughly and rub a blob of shampoo between your palms. Massage it gently into the scalp, describing little whirling motions all over the head. Squeeze the suds through from the roots of the hair to the tips, rinse thoroughly, then dry lightly with a warm towel. Take a tip from the animal kingdom and rediscover the delights of grooming each other – an art most humans now feel they have to pay for.

Water play

Sex aids and aphrodisiacs

A variety of sex aids or toys are sold over-the-counter in sex shops or by mail order through magazines. These include Chinese balls (a woman can wear them in her vagina where they vibrate slightly as she moves about during the day) and condoms with various protrusions on them, which are designed to stimulate the clitoris during intercourse. Other condoms are brightly coloured and flavoured with fruit.

The vibrator is by far the most popular sex toy. Shaped like a penis and battery-operated, it can be used in love play or for female masturbation. Some vibrators have an ejaculation mechanism. Many sex therapists advise the use of a vibrator for women learning to give themselves orgasms.

To help maintain erection, the simple ring designed to fit at the base of the penis is probably the only useful device. A piece of ribbon will do equally well. Tied fairly tightly around the penis, it acts as a one-way valve. Blood enters the penis but is prevented from leaving it, and thus the erection is maintained for a little longer. A variety of creams and sprays which claim to prolong erections or to trigger orgasms are also available.

Named after Aphrodite, the Greek goddess of love, aphrodisiacs are drugs claimed to excite lust. They may also be taken to stave off exhaustion or heighten pleasure during sex. The popularity of these drugs throughout history is a testimony to the fickleness of human sexual chemistry.

In some civilizations, highly nutritious foods were regarded as the most reliable stimulants, and may indeed have had a beneficial effect on people whose diet was usually poor. The Greeks went for eggs, honey, snails, and shellfish such as mussels and crabs. One Arab recipe from The Perfumed Garden recommends a glass of very thick honey, twenty almonds and a hundred pine nuts to be taken for three nights on retiring. Other recipes were to be applied externally. In order

Ringing the changes

'to increase the dimensions of small members and make them splendid', the author of *The Perfumed Garden* advised rubbing the penis with the melted down fat from the hump of a camel, bruised leeches, asses' members, and even hot pitch. These 'rubs' were probably less effective than the treatment of rubbing itself.

The Chinese were more

scientific in their approach. They measured and blended the powdered roots of plants, then gave them colourful names like 'the bald chicken drug'. This drug got its name when a septuagenarian civil servant who took it regularly, fathered three sons and paid so much attention to his wife that she could no longer either sit or lie down. He was forced to throw the remains of the drug out into the yard, where it was gobbled up by the cockerel. The cock jumped on a hen straight away, and continued mating with it for several days without interruption, all the while pecking at its head to keep its balance, until the chicken was completely bald, whereupon the cockerel fell off. The proud inventor of the drug claimed that if it was taken three times a day for sixty days, a man would be able to satisfy 40 women.

Horns have long been thought to have aphrodisiac properties because of
their obvious phallic shape. Continuing belief in the potency of rhinoceros horn has brought the single-horned African rhinoceros to the brink of extinction. In fact horn consists of fibrous tissue, similar in construction to hair and nails. Like them, rhino horn contains the protein keratin, and the minerals sulphur, calcium and phosphorus. The addition of these elements to a poor diet might improve vigour, but a cheese sandwich would do just as well.

Another famous aphrodisiac is Spanish fly, the common name of
the beetle cantharides. The beetle is dried and the active principal, cantharidin, is extracted. If swallowed, cantharidin causes an intense burning sensation in the throat, followed by diarrhoea. Then the urinogenital tract becomes so inflamed that urination becomes impossible. The penis ends up engorged and throbbing, but this is due to excruciating pain rather than to sexual urgency. Taking Spanish fly can sometimes be fatal.

Your sexual problems solved

The sexual relationship can be the greatest source of human pleasure, but it is also more fraught with

anxiety than most other human bonds. This section of the book looks at some commonly experienced problems, both medical and emotional.

Female orgasm

Since the 1960s, when Kinsey began to bring sex out of the closet, there has been such a great deal of open discussion centred around the female orgasm that many women feel under intense pressure to 'perform'. If you feel your partner is comparing you to previous lovers, or to an orgasmic ideal in his head, it detracts from the intimate pleasure of sex and turns it into a competition.

Many women are bothered by the idea that there may be two types of orgasm – vaginal and clitoral. They wonder whether the orgasms they are experiencing are 'the real thing'. But are there really two types of orgasm? It was Freud who first suggested that there were. He said that the orgasm experienced through clitoral stimulation was the precursor of a deeper, more satisfying orgasm experienced in the vagina during penetration by the penis. According to him, the vaginal orgasm was a 'true, mature' sexual response, while the clitoral orgasm was its immature inferior. The value judgements Freud and his followers placed on the two types of orgasm have caused a lot of unhappiness among some women who never experience orgasm during penetration. They feel that they are missing out, and are therefore inadequate: less than 'real women'.

Researchers into sexual response have been much concerned with the categorization of the female orgasm since Freud's time. Kinsey's view was that there was only one type of orgasm, that it was triggered by clitoral stimulation and involved contractions of all parts of the female body, including the vagina. He could not distinguish a second type of orgasm that centred solely on the vagina, and he utterly refuted Freud's distinction between 'mature' and 'immature' orgasms.

Subsequent clinical evidence has proved conclusively that Kinsey was right, and now sexologists are generally agreed that an orgasm is an orgasm. Researcher Helen Kaplan has come to this conclusion: 'Regardless of how friction is applied to the clitoris, i.e. by the tongue, by the woman's finger or her partner's, by a vibrator, or by coitus, female orgasm is probably always evoked by clitoral stimulation. However, it is always expressed by circumvaginal muscle discharge.'

Female orgasm

Although all orgasms are equal, women do report different sensations according to whether they are being penetrated or masturbated. And the surprise is that masturbatory orgasms, which are experienced by all women who can teach themselves to come through masturbation, alone or with a partner, are the more pleasurably acute. All women who orgasm in this

way know the acute tension of the clitoris, the voluptuous rushing sensation that breaks into multiple contractions of the surrounding tissue. A small minority of women (around 20 per cent, according to sex researcher Shere Hite), who also orgasm with a penis inside the vagina, describe that as a quite different experience. Although Freud claimed that orgasms during intercourse were superior, the majority of women in a survey carried out by Shere Hite said they were less intense. Whereas masturbatory orgasm is experienced as a high, sweet, rippling sensation, the peak of sensitivity, orgasm with penetration is like the boom of a distant explosion, powerful, but somewhat muffled.

Orgasms triggered by the partner's fingers or tongue, and by masturbation, are probably more intense because stimulation is more localized and more sensitively guided. Masters and Johnson reported stronger contraction spasms and higher rates of heartbeat during orgasm without intercourse, and especially during masturbation, and many women confirmed that they had their best orgasms when alone. Orgasm during penetration is undoubtedly quite rare for many women because a thrusting penis can stimulate the clitoris only 'in passing', if at all, depending on the position of the couple. The orgasm experienced may be more diffuse because the penis alters the focus of attention from the clitoris to the whole of the lower part of the woman's body, and because the vagina is full, 'muffling' the sensation.

A simultaneous orgasm, when both partners come together during penetration, may feel like a surprisingly big underground explosion, but it

Your sexual problems solved

probably offers the least in terms of sensual awareness. The reason for this is that if both parties are focused on their own experience or 'black-out' and become oblivious of each other, the sensation of the partner's orgasm is largely lost. For a woman, simultaneous orgasm is often followed by a feeling of disorientation, and a disappointment that lovemaking has come to an end.

Orgasm during intercourse is often less acute. However, many of
the women who are able to experience it prefer it for emotional reasons, because it involves complete body-to-body contact, holding the partner and giving oneself to him at the same time. Feeling whole and loved and emotionally satisfied are important aspects of a good sexual relationship, but these feelings can be experienced whether orgasm takes place during intercourse or not. What is important is that women should experience regular masturbatory orgasms. Orgasm relieves tension, recharges the body and revitalizes the mind. It leaves the woman feeling sparkling and whole. When shared with a partner, it represents the peak of sexual fulfilment and can be a powerful expression of love, helping to unite the couple.

Multiple and sequential orgasms, like vaginal and clitoral
orgasms, are concepts which have caused a lot of confusion and left many women worried that their sexual response might be somewhat inadequate. Because orgasms come in waves, some women are not even sure whether their orgasms are multiple or single. Multiple orgasms are those that are experienced in a chain, one directly after another; sequential orgasms are those with a gap of a few minutes between each one. It seems that true multiple orgasm is extremely rare, although many women are capable of sequential orgasm.

On the topic of multiple orgasm, Masters and Johnson wrote: 'If
a female who is capable of having regular orgasms is properly stimulated within a short period after her first climax, she will in most instances be capable of having a second, third, fourth, and even a fifth and sixth orgasm before she is fully satiated. As contrasted with the male's usual inability to have more than one orgasm in a short period, many females, especially when clitorally stimulated, can regularly have five or six full orgasms within a matter of minutes.'

Being capable of six orgasms in a row is not the same as
needing or even wanting that many. According to Shere Hite, about 90 per cent of women who orgasm feel completely satisfied with a single climax. And in many women the clitoris remains hypersensitive, and further stimulation is uncomfortable and can even prove painful.

Premature ejaculation

Anxiety is often the cause of premature ejaculation. In an extramarital relationship a man may ejaculate as soon as he penetrates his partner's vagina, despite the fact that he does not have this problem with his wife. This is a sign of guilt. A man may also ejaculate before he wishes to if he feels frightened that his technique is not good enough, and ejaculating quickly will prevent him from having to reveal his lack of experience.

Believing that sex is bad because of what you were told as a child is another possible cause of premature ejaculation. If as a boy, you were punished for masturbating, you may have taught yourself to come quickly to lessen the chance of being found out and to minimize the guilt you felt at your own pleasure.

Fear of getting too close to another person may also be a contributing factor. Intimacy always brings with it the risk of loss, and the unbearable pain attendant on that loss. Subconsciously, a man who gets sex over with quickly may be trying to protect himself from close emotional involvement.

Several techniques can help men last longer, and these should be used in conjunction with examining the cause of the problem. Understanding what is wrong often brings its own release.

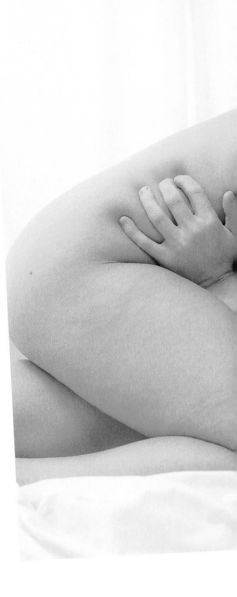

The stop-start technique for delaying ejaculation

The aim of these exercises is to learn to keep yourself below the point at which ejaculation seems inevitable for as long as possible. The first three steps can be practised by men who do not have a partner. In themselves, they will help you gain a greater measure of control. For the final four steps you will need the co-operation of a partner.

• **Step one** Masturbate with a dry hand. Avoid fantasizing, and concentrate instead on the sensation in your penis. Allow the pleasure to

Your sexual problems solved

build up but stop immediately you feel you are about to lose control. Relax for a while, still keeping your mind free of fantasies, until the danger of ejaculation has passed, then begin again. Following the same pattern, aim to continue stopping and starting for 15 minutes without orgasm. You may not be able to manage it at first, but keep trying. As you get more practised, you will probably find you have to stop less often. When you have completed three 15-minute sessions on three consecutive occasions (not necessarily one immediately after the other!), proceed to step two.

● **Step two** involves masturbating with a lubricating jelly to heighten sensation, and make delay more difficult. Follow the technique in step one until you have completed three separate consecutive sessions as above.

● **Step three** You will now have gained a good measure of control. The next step involves masturbating with a dry hand for 15 minutes before ejaculation. Keep focusing on your penis rather than fantasizing. When you feel yourself getting dangerously excited, don't stop, but instead, change rhythm or alter your strokes in such a way that the pressure to ejaculate fades. Experiment to see which strokes excite you most, and which allow you most control. Work on this step until you have completed three consecutive sessions as before.

• **Step four** Now involve your partner. Lie on your back and get her to masturbate you with a dry hand, as in step one. Concentrate on the sensations in your penis and ask her to stop every time you get too aroused before the 15 minutes is up. The aim is to last for three consecutive 15-minute sessions.

• **Step five** Repeat step four, but ask your partner to use a lubricant while she masturbates you. You will find ejaculation much more difficult to control, and you may have to ask her to stop more often. Once you have mastered three consecutive 15-minute sessions, you are ready to try the stop-start technique with intercourse.

• **Step six** The best position for delaying ejaculation is with the woman on top. Once you are inside her, ask her to move gently. Put your hands on her hips so that you can let her know with your hands when you want her to stop, and when you are ready for her to start again. Again, aim to last for 15 minutes, but if you can't, don't worry; you can start again once you recover your erection, and the second time you will probably have more control. During intercourse, concentrate entirely on yourself. Give your partner your full concentration and bring her to orgasm either before or afterwards, with oral or manual stimulation.

• **Step seven** Move on to other positions. It is more difficult to delay ejaculation with the man on top, so save this until last.

The squeeze technique for delaying ejaculation

The 'squeeze' action is designed to cause your erection to subside, and it can be applied every time you get too close to ejaculation. Your partner performs the squeeze by gripping your penis firmly, and pressing with her thumb on the frenulum. This is the place on the underside of the penis where the head joins the shaft. At the same time, she presses on the opposite side of the penis with her forefinger, and with her other fingers curled round the shaft. It is important that she presses fairly hard on the penis and doesn't move her hand while doing so. Too light a touch could cause you to ejaculate straight away.

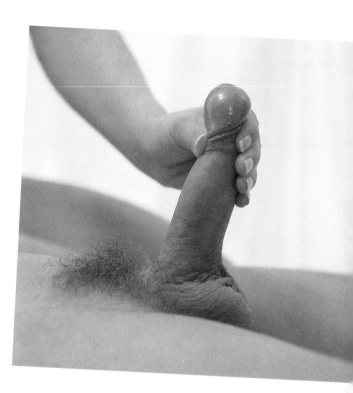

- **Step one** Get your partner to masturbate you with a dry hand. Any time you get too close to ejaculation, signal to her to stop and squeeze your penis. As with the stop-start technique, aim to last for three consecutive 15-minute sessions before moving on to step two.

- **Step two** Get your partner to masturbate you slowly and gently as before, but this time ask her to use a lubricant. Follow the procedure for step one.

- **Step three** Now you are ready for intercourse, but not for thrusting. Instead, lie on your back and ask your partner to sit on top of you, with your penis inside her. Neither of you should move. As soon as you feel the urge to come, your partner should rise off you (this movement is dangerous as it applies stimulation), and immediately hold your penis in the squeeze grip. Repeat the exercise a couple of times before you allow yourself to ejaculate.

- **Step four** When you feel more confident about your self-control, ask your partner to move gently while she sits on top of you in the same position. When you feel the urge to ejaculate, she should move off you and squeeze as before, until you can last 15 minutes without ejaculating.

- **Step five** You are now ready to try other positions, but remember that with the man on top, you will have least control. As with the stop-start technique, during intercourse you should focus all attention on yourself. Your partner will not feel neglected if you bring her to orgasm orally or manually either before or after intercourse.

Contraception

The ovulation testing pack

is a completely new method of natural family planning that allows you to enjoy making love without using any contraceptives on most days of your cycle. The pack includes a personal monitor that checks your urine samples and analyses them to indicate the days of the month on which you are likely to get pregnant. You should use contraceptives if you wish to make love on those days. The pack is 93–95 per cent reliable and very easy to use.

The ovulation testing pack includes a monitor which works by reading test sticks which collect hormones from your early morning urine. The display screen shows a yellow light when a urine test is needed, a red light when you are likely to conceive, and a green light when it is safe for you to have sex without using contraception. The monitor is no bigger than your hand.

Natural family planning, by

contrast, requires meticulous record-keeping and iron self-discipline. It involves charting your temperature day by day throughout the menstrual cycle to discover the period of ovulation, during which you must abstain from sex. Any unpredictable irregularity in the cycle can carry the risk of pregnancy.

The Pill is up to 99 per cent reliable. It allows for completely

spontaneous lovemaking. The freedom it gives is of enormous psychological benefit in any relationship. The Pill also regulates the menstrual cycle and reduces period pain and heavy bleeding in many women. Mild side effects occur in some women who take the Pill, but they usually disappear after a few months. They may include nausea, headaches, depression, weight gain and some bleeding between periods. If side-effects persist, the doctor or clinic will usually recommend a change of contraception. Before your doctor prescribes the Pill, he or she will ask for your medical history, including incidence of thrombosis in your family. The health risks involved in taking the Pill are slight when compared to the risks of pregnancy and childbirth.

The combined Pill contains synthetic forms of the sex hormones

oestrogen and progesterone, which interfere with the woman's regular 28-day menstrual cycle. In a woman who is not taking the Pill, production of the sex hormones fluctuates during the cycle, and it is this fluctuation that triggers ovulation. When the hormone level is kept artificially constant by the Pill, the signal to ovulate is cancelled out. The same happens during

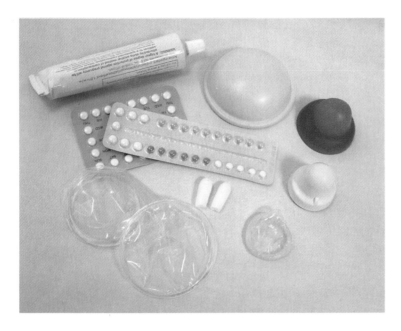

Contraceptives available from your doctor or family planning clinic include the Pill, the cap or diaphragm and the male and female condom. The illustration shows two designs of cap and a diaphragm, all of which are used with spermicide, which comes in a tube or as pessaries. The combined Pill comes in packs of 21, which gives you one week a month without pills. The progestogen-only Pill is taken every day and comes in packs of 28. The male condom is shown unrolled, as it comes out of the sterile pack, and the female condom is shown opened out. It fits like a bag inside the vagina.

pregnancy, which is why overlapping pregnancies do not occur. Anyone who smokes heavily may be at risk of thrombosis, smokers and those who are over 35 are often advised not to take the combined Pill.

The 'progestogen-only Pill' is not, as sometimes assumed, a low-dose Pill, but one containing a single hormone, progestogen. It has the effect of thickening the secretions in the cervix, which makes it difficult for sperm to pass. It can be taken by breastfeeding mothers, unlike the combined Pill, which suppresses lactation.

The condom is 85–98 per cent effective as a method of contraception. Condoms work by preventing the sperm from getting to its destination, and they do not interfere with the body's chemistry. The condom is also the key to safe sex as it protects against all sexually transmitted diseases. For more details about condoms and how to use them, see page 128.

Caps and diaphragms act as a contraceptive by forming a barrier across the neck of the womb (cervix), which prevents the sperm from reaching and fertilizing the egg. A good fit is crucial. You need to be examined by your doctor or family planning clinic so that the right-sized cap or diaphragm can be chosen, and you can be shown how to insert it. A cap or diaphragm should always be used with a spermicide. This

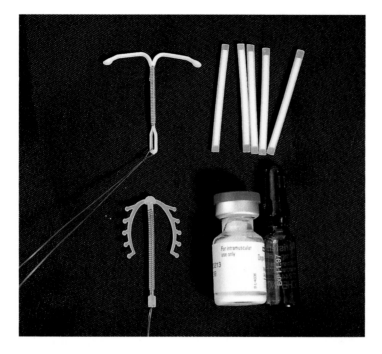

The contraceptives shown here need expert fitting or administration from your family planning clinic and are then effective long-term. On the left are two types of IUD ('U' shaped and 'T' shaped), which are pushed up inside the uterus. Hormonal implants, which are fitted under the skin of the upper arm are shown top right, and below them, small vials containing hormonal injections.

combination has been found to be a 95 per cent safe contraceptive.
Smear a little spermicide on to the diaphragm and around the rim, to facilitate insertion. Squeeze the diaphragm into a boat shape and insert it as you would a sanitary tampon, opening the lips of the vagina with one hand. When the rim rests behind the pubic bone at the front and the dome covers the cervix at the back, it is in place. Doctors recommend that you should not leave the diaphragm or cap in place for longer than 24 hours, but you should wait for at least six hours after intercourse before removing it. Remember that spermicide will be effective only for about three hours, so you will need to put more into the vagina if you have intercourse after the diaphragm or cap has been in place for that length of time. When you remove the diaphragm or cap, wash it carefully in warm soapy water and allow it to dry in a warm place, or pat gently with a towel.

The female condom is as effective as other barrier methods. It lines
the vagina and has an inner ring that sits over the cervix and an outer ring that lies flat against the labia. The female condom is made of colourless odourless polyurethane. The woman pushes the condom up inside her vagina before intercourse, and afterwards removes it and disposes of it. Like the male condom, the female condom is not reusable. It comes ready lubricated for easy insertion and no spermicide is necessary. Female condoms are made in one size only and will fit all women. During intercourse, it is a good idea for the woman to guide the man's penis into the condom to make sure it does not enter the vagina outside the condom. As the female condom is loose-

Your sexual problems solved

fitting, it will move during sex, but you will still be protected, because the penis stays inside the condom. To remove the condom after sex, simply twist the outer ring to keep the semen inside, and pull the condom out gently.

The IUD (intra-uterine device) or coil is a small plastic and copper device that is inserted into the womb to prevent conception. This can be done only by a doctor trained in family planning. The IUD comes compressed in a thin tube, which is slid through the cervical canal into the uterus and then withdrawn, leaving the IUD to spring into shape. Thin threads hang from the IUD about 3cm/ 1 inch into the vagina, and these can be felt with the fingers to make sure that the device is still in place. To remove an IUD, the doctor pulls the strings with a specially designed instrument. Depending on type, IUDs are usually replaced about every five years. The IUD is reckoned to be 96–99 per cent effective as a contraceptive, although it is not clear exactly how it works. Many women like it because it allows both partners to be spontaneous in their lovemaking. However, it does not suit everyone. Some women experience discomfort and bleeding for a few hours or days after the IUD is inserted, and one in four women have to have it removed because of acute pain and heavy bleeding. Sometimes an IUD may fall out; this is more likely to happen during a period than at any other time, and this is why it is important to check regularly that the thin strings are still inside the vagina.

Contraceptive injections may be given with a drug that contains hormones of the progestogen type. An injection is needed every 8–12 weeks and is a virtually 100 per cent reliable contraceptive. However, it often has a disruptive effect on a woman's menstrual cycle, making periods more frequent or even disappear altogether. Return of regular periods may be delayed for up to a year after the last injection.

Contraceptive implants release a hormone into the bloodstream. The implants are small, stick-like and pliable, and are inserted under the skin of the inner upper arm by your doctor or clinic in a simple, almost pain free procedure. They cannot be seen. The effects will last for up to five years, and although the implants can be removed at any time, the body will not be free of the hormone for a short time afterwards. Implants are more than 99 per cent reliable, although they may make periods less regular or disappear altogether. These side effects may settle down after several months.

Emergency contraception is also called the 'morning-after Pill'. This last-resort method can be used if intercourse has taken place without contraception or if the usual method has failed, say in the event of a burst condom. It may also be prescribed to a woman after a sexual assault. It can be given up to 72 hours after intercourse and is 96-99 per cent effective.

Safer sex

A fulfilling sexual relationship

can help boost good health, but sex and health are also connected in other ways that require serious consideration. The two major areas of concern are contraception and protection against sexually transmitted diseases, especially AIDS.

AIDS is at present an incurable condition that is usually fatal in the long term. It is transmitted by having unprotected sex with someone who is infected with HIV, the AIDS virus. As there are no immediate symptoms of the disease, it is not possible to tell who has already contracted it. This means that unprotected sex with any new partner carries a risk. The only way to be absolutely sure that you do not catch the HIV virus or AIDS is to use a condom every time you have sex. Some couples who do not wish to use a condom decide to take an AIDS test at a clinic for sexually transmitted diseases to make sure they are both clear of the virus.

With unprotected sex, you are at risk not only from your present partner, but from each of his or her previous partners over the past four years. If you become infected you can infect your next four years' worth of partners, and any children they might bear, without even knowing it.

A recent survey carried out among young people showed that the majority of sexually active young women had taken responsibility for contraception by being on the Pill, but that though they were aware of the

danger of AIDS, young people often had sex with a new partner without a condom, particularly if they had been drinking. It is important to remember that AIDS is much more dangerous to your health than pregnancy, and unlike pregnancy, there is no way that the disease can be terminated.

The message is clear: anyone who engages in casual sex or is having sex with a new partner should use a condom even if contraceptive protection is provided by the Pill. Women as well as men are recommended to carry condoms with them.

Clean bodies are generally more appealing than dirty ones, though the smell of a lover's sweat can have aphrodisiac qualities. Bathing is not always practicable or desirable, but you should always wash the genitals and anus before sex, to protect against infection, to increase the enjoyment of your partner and to give self confidence. Soap and water are all that is needed. Deodorants and perfumes kill the body's delightful natural scents, and they also taste unpleasant. Vaginal deodorants can be positively harmful, destroying the micro-organisms in the vagina that protect against disease. Always wash anything that is inserted in the anus, as anal sex carries the highest risk of infection.

How to use a condom

Condoms come ready-rolled and most end in a teat, which catches the semen.

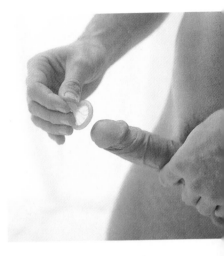

- **Expel the air** from the teat at the tip of the condom by squeezing it.

- **Place the opening** of the condom on the head of the penis.

- **Unroll it down the shaft** to fit comfortably.

- **When fully unrolled,** the condom should extend almost to the base of the penis and fit like a second skin, feeling silky and smooth.

After ejaculation, the condom should be removed carefully to prevent spillage. First, the man withdraws his penis from the woman's vagina, holding the condom securely to his penis so as not to leave it behind. Then he removes it and disposes of it. Of course, care must always be taken that any semen left on the penis does not get transferred – on the fingers, for example – to the woman's vagina.

Putting on a condom can be fun. Some women enjoy doing this for their partners. You can use your lips and tongue to help your fingers unroll the condom down the shaft of the penis – but be careful not to snag the delicate material with your nails or jewellery.

Sexually transmitted diseases

The symptoms of sexually transmitted diseases (STD) are often impossible to detect initially, but if your partner is infected, or you have a sexual relationship with someone who is promiscuous, then a check-up is essential. If symptoms do manifest themselves, they are likely to take the form of a discharge from the vagina, penis or anus, or itching or soreness around the genitals or anus, or a lump or rash on the genitals, anus or mouth.

If you suspect you may have a sexually transmitted disease, you should see your doctor or clinic straight away. You can find the telephone number of your nearest clinic by looking up 'special clinic', 'venereal disease' or 'VD' in the telephone directory, or by phoning your local hospital. You will be tested as quickly as possible, and if the test is positive, you will be advised to contact your recent sexual partners, as they too may need treatment. Avoid sex until you are clear of the disease.

AIDS stands for Acquired Immune Deficiency Syndrome, and the disease is caused by the human immuno-deficiency virus, known as HIV. Once it is inside the body, this virus invades the white blood cells, which normally fight off disease, then it multiplies and destroys them. It also breeds inside the brain. Three to four years normally elapse between infection with HIV and any subsequent development of the symptoms associated with AIDS.

As AIDS develops the body's natural defences become depleted, and the AIDS patient is increasingly likely to contract diseases that a healthy body would normally ward off, and so rare forms of cancer and pneumonia develop. Sometimes AIDS patients are attacked by several infections at once, such as candida, herpes and TB. At the same time, the brain may succumb to increasingly severe dementia. Somewhere between one in ten and one in three of those infected with HIV are likely to develop AIDS. As yet there is no cure for AIDS. AIDS usually progresses through various infections and stages of increasing debility to the eventual death of the sufferer.

How to avoid AIDS
- Always use a condom.
- Avoid anal sex.
- Don't share toothbrushes, razors or any other instrument that might transfer blood from cuts or abrasions.

The virus is present in body fluids, primarily semen and blood. It may also be present in saliva, though research indicates that saliva seems to

present little risk. Having anal intercourse with an infected partner is the most likely way of catching AIDS, and 80 per cent of British cases *so far* have been male homosexuals.

The second most common way of contracting the disease is through infected

blood. Almost a quarter of Britain's haemophiliac population now carry HIV because they have been injected with the clotting agent collected from infected blood. (Haemophiliacs are born without the blood-clotting factor, and can suffer severe bruising from a minor injury, and bleed to death from a cut unless they receive the clotting factor from donated blood.) HIV in the blood may also be transmitted on infected needles, and drug addicts are the third most highly at risk group of the population.

To become HIV positive you do not have to be homosexual or

promiscuous, a drug addict or a haemophiliac. Heterosexuals are also at risk. Even a heterosexual in a steady relationship stands the risk of contracting the disease if their partner has been infected in a previous relationship. Therefore when embarking on any new relationship, it is safest to wear a condom.

Gonorrhoea is caused by the bacterium gonococcus, which cannot

survive outside the body and is transmitted only by sexual intercourse, and never (as is sometimes imagined) on toilet seats or towels. In men the urethra, along which urine passes from the bladder, is infected, and there is sometimes pain on urinating and a thick discharge from the penis within a week after infection. In homosexual men the rectum may be infected, with the possibility of irritation and discharge from the anus. In women, gonorrhoea infects the cervix, urethra and rectum, and, as with men, there may be discharge and pain on urinating. If infection spreads to the uterus there is a 10 per cent chance that the fallopian tubes may be blocked, causing sterility. Often, however, there are no symptoms in either men or women.

The treatment for gonorrhoea is usually a single dose of

antibiotics such as penicillin, with a check-up afterwards to make sure the infection has cleared. If gonorrhoea is not diagnosed and treated, serious complications can develop. Men may suffer epididymitis – pain and swelling in the testicles; women may suffer peritonitis – inflammation of the membranes of the abdomen. Both sexes could develop gonococcal septicaemia, an infection of the bloodstream with skin rashes and arthritis. In serious cases, sterility can result in both sexes. Pregnant women with gonorrhoea may pass it on to their babies, who can be born with gonococcal opthalmia, an acute inflammation of the eyes. Complications are, however, relatively rare nowadays.

Non-specific urethritis or NSU can be identified by lumps, soreness or itching around the genitals, anus or mouth. There may also be a discharge from the vagina or penis. The treatment is usually a two-week course of antibiotics for anyone who has had contact with an infected person. During treatment, patients are asked to give up alcohol, as this can bring about a recurrence of the symptoms. Complications can occur, and these are similar to those for gonorrhoea, but fortunately early diagnosis and treatment can prevent these. It is possible for a man to be periodically reinfected with NSU without changing his sex partner, and no explanation has so far been put forward for this. However, both partners will need treatment each time NSU manifests itself.

Syphilis is quite rare in Britain today. It affects women less than men, and its main victims are male homosexuals. Symptoms appear between 10 days and 12 weeks after infection. In the primary stage of the disease a small hard sore or chancre appears on the penis, vagina or rectum. It is painless and usually disappears very quickly. A few weeks later, in the secondary stage, the patient is feverish, with swollen glands and itching skin. The disease is curable with antibiotics, but if for some reason it should not be treated, serious complications will develop many years later. Until the advent of antibiotics, tertiary syphilis used to be quite common, with patients eventually suffering from dementia and dying a slow, agonizing death.

Chlamydia is one of the most common STDs and is caused by a bacterial parasite called chlamydia trachomatis. The disease is diagnosed by a swab test, and treatment is with antibiotics. Symptoms in men include a whitish yellow discharge from the penis, frequent 'burning' urination, and redness at the tip of the penis. Women may notice a discharge, a frequent need to urinate, and mild discomfort which they may mistake for vaginitis or menstrual cramps. However, many women experience no symptoms until they develop complications such as pelvic inflammatory disease, a serious condition which can result in infertility. Babies born to infected mothers may suffer from eye infection, which is sometimes serious, or pneumonia.

Genital herpes is a viral infection transmitted through sexual intercourse. It is very similar to the other sort of herpes, which causes cold sores, and can also be caught by having oral sex with someone who has active cold sores. The symptoms are itching, pain in the groin, discomfort on urinating and fever, followed by the appearance of painful red blisters on the vulva or penis, which burst to form ulcers. After about 10 days the symptoms disappear and the patient appears to be cured. But the infection is only lying dormant and may recur at any time, particularly when the patient is under stress. There is as yet no treatment for this disease. While the disease is dormant, it is safe to have sex without infecting one's partner, but it is impossible to predict the next attack, so the risk of infection remains. If the infection is active at the end of a pregnancy, a Caesarean section may be performed to prevent the baby becoming infected in the birth canal.

Genital warts are unpleasant but painless and can be treated quite easily. They are small lumps that appear on the penis, vulva, or anus and are mildly contagious. The treatment involves either painting the warts with a preparation called podophyllin, or freezing them off with liquid nitrogen. An association has been identified between genital warts and cervical cancer, so it is important to get rid of them as soon as possible, and to have regular cervical smears.

Thrush is a fungal infection that develops in certain conditions in the vagina. It is sometimes linked to taking the Pill, and if it recurs frequently, a different method of contraception may be advisable. A man may carry thrush, though he usually manifests no symptoms. Thrush causes vaginal soreness and itching, and a thick white discharge. The doctor will probably prescribe anti-fungal cream, to be used by both partners, and vaginal pessaries, though oral treatments are available too. Some women find that natural yoghurt in the vagina is effective. Avoid hot baths, and wearing tights, tight jeans and nylon knickers.

Trichomoniasis is one of the most common and least serious of all sexually transmitted diseases and may be passed on by bad hygiene practice in the use of towels as well as by sexual contact. It can exist in a symptom-free form and some people act as passive carriers for the disease. However, it can also cause discharge and pain in urinating in both sexes. Several drugs are available for treatment and their success rate is high.

Questions and answers

What happens when a man has a vasectomy?

A vasectomy is a very simple operation, more so than female sterilization. It can be performed under a local anaesthetic, and the patient can even watch what is happening – if he is not squeamish. He can be in and out of hospital within a 15 or 20 minute period.

Male sterilization is called 'vasectomy' because the tubes from the testes to the penis – the vas deferens – are cut and tied, or cauterized, or sealed electrically or chemically, to prevent sperm from leaving the body. The surgeon makes a small incision in the scrotum – either one in the middle or one at either side – to perform the operation, and closes the incision or incisions with a couple of stitches. The stitches are made of a material that is naturally absorbed by the body, so there is no need to have them removed later.

What happens after the operation?

After the operation, the patient is advised not to do any heavy work, including lifting, for a few days, but otherwise he can lead a perfectly normal life. He may experience some temporary bruising and swelling, but his sex life can be resumed as soon as he feels comfortable.

Vasectomy is not immediately effective, as there will inevitably be some live sperm present in the system, but after up to 36 ejaculations these will all have been expelled. Two or four months after the operation, the man will be asked to return to hospital for a sperm check, and until the all-clear is given, he is advised to continue with whatever contraceptive he was using before the operation. Two clear semen tests (no sperm seen) are required before the vasectomy is considered to have been successful.

Despite assurances to the contrary, many men worry that their sex lives will be affected by vasectomy. In fact, strength of erection, intensity of ejaculation and quantity of seminal fluid cannot be altered one way or the other by snipping the vas deferens; all that happens is that the fluid ejaculated no longer contains sperm. Sperm are still produced in the testes, but instead of being ejaculated, they are reabsorbed harmlessly into the body.

Your sexual problems solved

What happens during female sterilization?

The principal of female sterilization is to cut, cauterize or block the fallopian tubes so that sperm are prevented from reaching and fertilizing the eggs. Female sterilization always used to involve major abdominal surgery, with a week's stay in hospital and a long, gradual recovery. But since the 1960s a new technique called laparoscopy has been developed, which makes the operation a relatively minor one. It can be performed under general anaesthetic if both doctor and patient are agreeable.

A very small tube is inserted through a tiny incision near the navel, and the gynaecologist pumps a harmless gas through it into the patients abdomen. This pushes aside the intestines. He then inserts a viewing device called a laparoscope through the same incision: looking down it he can see the womb and fallopian tubes. Through a second small incision near the pubic hair line he inserts a sterilizing instrument and performs the operation. It is all over within 15 minutes or so, and the patient can soon resume a normal life.

As a method of contraception, is female sterilization an acceptable alternative to vasectomy?

No. Since the advent of laparoscopy, female sterilization has become a much less dangerous operation than it used to be. However, the vasectomy is a much simpler operation and should be preferred every time as a method of contraception, unless there are medical reasons that dictate otherwise.

What can be done to regulate prolonged and heavy periods?

A very good way of alleviating this problem is to go on the Pill. It has helped countless women worldwide to rid themselves of heavy period pain, to lighten the menstrual flow and to shorten the length of periods to only a few days.

What is PMT?

Premenstrual tension affects around 40 per cent of women with symptoms of tiredness, irritability, loss of libido and depression around the onset of their periods. In some women the symptoms are hardly apparent, but others almost reach breaking point, cannot cope with the normal stresses of everyday life and sometimes become aggressive or hysterical toward their partners and others.

These symptoms are caused by hormonal imbalance in the critical days before the period. Research has shown that PMT-sufferers tend to have lower than normal levels of progesterone and higher than normal levels of oestrogen. The discrepancy is felt on those days when the hormone levels are changing very rapidly.

What to do if you suffer from PMT

• Keep a record of your symptoms, such as headache and tension, in a menstrual diary. As far as you can, avoid planning any events which may prove demanding on days when you are likely to be feeling below your best. Take as much rest on these days as possible.

• Discuss your feelings with your partner, and with your doctor, and ask for support from the first and treatment from the second. Your doctor may suggest a course of progesterone.

• Eat a healthy diet rich in wholegrains, fresh fruit and vegetables. Avoid too many salty foods and limit your fluid intake from the middle of your cycle. Foods rich in potassium, such as beans, potatoes, fish and nuts, will help combat fluid retention.

What happens at the menopause?

The menopause is when periods stop and a woman is no longer able to bear children. Ageing causes the ovaries to stop releasing eggs at around 49 years old. Every woman is born with millions of egg follicles in her ovaries, and around 480 of these are released during a lifetime's ovulation. At the menopause the remaining egg follicles degenerate, and there are lower levels of oestrogen and progesterone circulating in the bloodstream. The reduction in hormone levels is sometimes responsible for unpleasant symptoms such as vaginal dryness, hot flushes and loss of libido. Periods may stop suddenly, never to resume, or they may become gradually lighter, and further and further apart. If there is any irregular bleeding, bleeding after intercourse or very heavy bleeding, you should see your doctor for a check up straight away, as this is abnormal. Menopausal symptoms can be banished by taking hormone replacement therapy (HRT). If intercourse is painful, a lubricating jelly or vaginal hormone cream prescribed by your doctor can help.

Does the G-spot really exist?

The G-spot is named after its discoverer, Ernst Grafenberg. While many women still doubt its existence, others claim that stimulating a place about 5cm/2 inches inside the vagina towards the front of the body gives them intense pleasure.

The G-spot is said to be the female equivalent of the male prostate gland, which is situated about 5cm/2 inches up the rectum towards the front of the body. Stimulation of both these places can lead to orgasm in some cases. Some women have even found that they ejaculate a fluid if they have an orgasm by stimulation of the G-spot, and researchers in Canada and the United States claim that the composition of the fluid is remarkably similar to the secretion of the prostate gland.

How do you find the G-spot?

If you doubt the existence of the G-spot, you can try to find it yourself. The easiest way to reach it is with your own or your partner's finger, but there are also positions for intercourse in which the penis stimulates the sensitive area. Rear-entry is best, particularly with the man on top and a pillow beneath your hips, so that the penis presses against the front wall of the vagina.

What if a woman is not interested in sex?

We are all sexual beings and have the potential to be interested in sex all our lives. If a woman does not enjoy sex, perhaps her partner needs to become a more sensitive and reassuring lover, in which case reading this book should help. If a woman has grown bored with sex, it may be that she is no longer interested in her partner. Then, no matter how good his understanding of the female body and its responses, he will get no passion from her.

Sex performed for the sake of holding a delicate relationship together could not be further removed from a good, exciting and fulfilling sex life. Masturbation can be more fun than sex performed just for the sake of it. If you are in this situation, then it is probably time to ask yourself whether you intend to remain in it, and to start talking with your partner about the possibilities for improvement, if they exist, or for parting if they don't. Alternatively, you may come to the conclusion, independently or together, that you prefer the status quo to the alternative trauma of splitting up. In this case, you should be prepared for the possibility of the frustrated partner seeking sexual satisfaction outside the relationship.

Why do men sometimes lose interest in sex?

Because male sexual response is more straightforward than female sexual response, it is somehow assumed that men are always ready to have sex 'on demand'. Their partners can be very disappointed to find that this is not necessarily so. This can be a problem, particularly for women in their middle years who have developed a strong sexual drive. A partner who is repeatedly too tired or uninspired for sex can cause such women deep unhappiness and frustration.

The problem can be partly due to conditioning. In the case of a second marriage, for instance, where a couple have been passionately adulterous lovers and are now married themselves, the man may revert to the way he was with his first wife, with whom he rarely made love. If his new wife cannot help him overcome the problem of being attracted only to the forbidden, she may wish to persuade him to seek professional help.

Although every man is likely to suffer a temporary loss of interest in sex from time to time, due to the stress of overwork, or to feeling tired or under the weather, the cause of a more sustained loss of interest probably lies in the relationship itself. No one can make love with someone they feel angry with or hostile towards, and personal problems need to be resolved before a good sex life can be resumed.

What is a woman's likely reaction to rape and what emotional help can be given?

The woman's personality and the manner in which she is raped affect her reaction. Sometimes women are raped by a lover who refuses to take no for an answer. Violent sex can even become a way of life, leaving women with a feeling of utter worthlessness. If attacked by a vicious prowler or intruder, a woman usually submits out of a profound sense of terror of being killed or maimed, which is even greater than the fear of being sexually defiled. Immediately after the rape she may feel happy to be alive, but this is usually followed by an unnatural calm or unconsolable distress and self-disgust. Shock is often followed by anger and a paranoid fear that rape may happen all over again. There may be a dread of being left alone and an obsessional desire to wash, bathe and clean the house in an attempt to rid herself of the defilement. Guilt is a very common reaction. A rape victim can easily blame herself – for being with the wrong man, for being gullible, for not raising the alarm or for shouting too much and, in doing so, provoking her attacker.

Rape can profoundly affect a woman's sex life. She may seize up at any sexual advance from her partner, or, feeling that her body has become contaminated and worthless, she may have indiscriminate sex with many partners. She is likely to feel depressed. All these symptoms are part of what is called rape trauma syndrome, and they may last for months or even years.

The partner and close friends or family of the victim may also feel anger and guilt. It is best not to give vent to these feelings repeatedly in front of the woman who has been raped, as they will only reinforce her own feelings of powerlessness. The worst thing you can do is to blame the victim for what has happened to her. She will be harbouring enough doubts about herself without hearing them from you.

Rape is a profoundly shattering experience, and anyone who has suffered it needs patience and understanding, careful and sympathetic listening and gentle encouragement. Time and understanding will bring healing.

Your sexual problems solved

INDEX

Acknowledgements

Publishing Director: Laura Bamford

Commissioning Editor: Jane McIntosh
Assistant Editor: Catharine Davey

Art Director: Keith Martin
Senior Designer: Ben Barrett
Designer: Steve Byrne

Photography: Peter Pugh-Cook
Photography (pages 60–73): Richard Truscott

Stylist: Sheila Birkenshaw
Picture Researchers: Sally Claxton and Wendy Gay

Production Controller: Dawn Mitchell

The publishers would like to thank the following
organisations for their kind permission to reproduce
photographs in this book:
Gaze International/Gordon Rainsford p 36
Image Bank/G & M David de Lossy p 43

The publishers would like to thank all those companies and
individuals who supplied props for photography,
and in particular:
Ann Summers for the loan of clothing
Berkertex at Littlewoods for the loan of bed linen
Boots The Chemists for the provision of contraceptives
British Home Stores for the loan of bed linen and towels
The Futon Shop for the provision of furniture
George at Asda for the loan of clothing
Hom for the loan of clothing
Jockey for Men for the loan of clothing
Jockey for Women for the loan of clothing
Knickerbox for the loan of clothing
Marie Stopes International for the loan of contraceptives
Next for the loan of bed linen and clothing
Nice Irma's for the loan of soft furnishings
River Island Clothing Co. for the loan of clothing
RJ's Homeshop for the loan of furniture
Sloggi for Men for the loan of clothing
Unipath Ltd for the provision of the Persona ovulation
testing pack (exclusively available at Boots The Chemists)